'Give me your hand,' Michael ordered.

Rosalind placed her left hand on his open palm.

Michael looked down at the slender fingers laid on his and told himself not to think of how different things might have been if she had married him five years ago. Then this would have been a real ceremony, and the ring would have symbolised love and trust and commitment. All the things that Rosalind didn't believe in, he reminded himself brutally, and pushed the ring brusquely onto her third finger before he had a chance to change his mind.

'With this ring, I thee disguise,' he muttered, in an attempt to defuse the moment.

'Just for a month,' Rosalind added, sounding oddly breathless, and he nodded.

'Just for a month.'

Jessica Hart had a haphazard career before she began writing to finance a degree in history. Her experience ranged from waitress, theatre production assistant and outback cook to newsdesk secretary, expedition PA and English teacher, and she has worked in countries as different as France and Indonesia, Australia and Cameroon. She now lives in the north of England, where her hobbies are limited to eating and drinking and travelling when she can, preferably to places where she'll find good food, or desert or tropical rain.

Recent titles by the same author:

BIRTHDAY BRIDE
TEMPORARY ENGAGEMENT
OUTBACK HUSBAND

MARRIED FOR A MONTH

BY
JESSICA HART

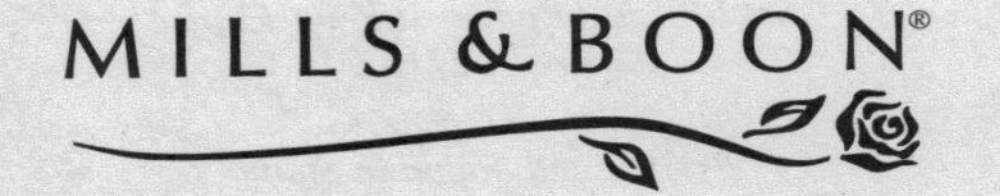

First published in Great Britain 1999
Harlequin Mills & Boon Limited,
Eton House, 18-24 Paradise Road, Richmond, Surrey TW9 1SR

ISBN 0 263 81736 9

Set in Times Roman 10½ on 12 pt.
02-9907-52718 C1

Printed and bound in Spain
by Litografia Rosés, S.A., Barcelona

CHAPTER ONE

'YOU remember Rosalind, don't you?'

Michael froze. Tired of sitting still after long hours in the plane, he had got to his feet when Emma went to answer the door, and was standing by the window, rubbing his neck wearily and wondering if he could face the business of hiring a car that morning. There had been nothing to warn him, no premonition when the doorbell had rung, that the life he had built so carefully for the last five years was about to come crashing down around him.

Very slowly, his hand fell from his neck and he turned, hoping against hope that he had misheard the name, but there she was, walking past Emma into the room as if she owned it. Rosalind.

Rosalind, with long hair the colour of beech leaves. Rosalind, with the witchy green eyes and the smile that still haunted his dreams. Rosalind, whom he had tried so hard to forget.

'Hello, Michael,' she said.

Only Rosalind had ever been able to stand like that, so sure of her own beauty, so certain of getting whatever she wanted. She looked as if she were waiting for him to throw himself at her feet.

If so, she was in for a long wait, Michael told himself grimly. He had been at Rosalind's feet before, and it had been a bitter and humiliating experience, one he had no intention of repeating.

'Rosalind,' he replied, his voice empty of all expression.

He felt jarred, faintly sick, as if he had run smack against a wall in the dark, but when he glanced accusingly at his sister she was smiling, looking from one to the other with nothing but pleasure, anticipation, and a dawning puzzlement at his less than enthusiastic response to her surprise in her shining, open face.

'It must be years since you two have met,' Emma was saying. 'Why don't you catch up with each other while I go and make some coffee?'

Rosalind eyed Michael with dismay. She had been so nervous about seeing him again that she had been absurdly relieved when she walked into the room to find that he looked just the same. The same quiet, intelligent face with the alert pale grey eyes. The same compact body. The same air of stillness and self-containment that was at once intriguing and intimidating.

But now she could see that he had changed after all. The grey eyes were shuttered, his expression guarded, his mouth hard. 'Emma, I don't think this is such a good idea,' she began, but Emma was already at the door.

'Michael's never let me down yet,' she said with a reassuring smile. 'All you have to do is explain. And don't worry about Jamie, I'll keep an eye on him.'

Then she was gone, closing the door behind her, and Rosalind and Michael were left facing each other in wary silence.

It was hard to believe that they had ever laughed together, loved together. Rosalind could feel the hostility erected around Michael like an invisible barrier, and she wished Emma hadn't gone. Once she would have been sure of her ability to charm him against his will. In the past, all it had taken was a smile or a look or a single touch and Michael had allowed himself to be captivated. He wouldn't be captivated now, Rosalind knew, looking at that still, watchful figure by the window. She could tell by the way he stood there that he was on guard against her.

But she had to try.

'How have you been, Michael?' she asked at last.

'I've been fine.'

Rosalind suppressed a flicker of irritation at the sardonic edge to Michael's voice. Maybe it *had* been an inane question, but she had to start somewhere.

'Good.' She hesitated, chewing her lip uncertainly. He was supposed to ask how *she* was now, and give her the opening she needed, but Michael clearly had no intention of following the conventions of pleasant conversation. He just stood there, his mouth set in that forbidding line and his eyes implacable. Rosalind suppressed a sigh. 'And your research?' she persevered. 'Are you working on an interesting site?'

Michael put his hands in his pockets and regarded her with deepening suspicion. 'I think it's interesting,' he said in the same cool voice. 'I doubt if you would.'

She hadn't been interested before, Rosalind admitted to herself with an inward grimace. She had never been able to understand what Michael saw in archaeology, just as he hadn't understood how she could be happy without a career. It was yet another example of how different their lives had been, how different they still were. Sometimes it seemed to Rosalind that all they had shared had been an intense physical attraction, and they didn't even have that any more, she realised with a touch of wistfulness. Michael was pointedly keeping his distance.

He wasn't saying anything or doing anything, but the

atmosphere was jangling with tension. Hoping that it would help if she looked more relaxed, Rosalind walked over to the sofa and sat down. Then she wished she hadn't. Michael ignored her gesture inviting him to join her, and she could hardly loll around on the cushions while he stood there by the window, a remote, unyielding figure who clearly had no intention of making things easy for her.

Covertly, she studied him from under her lashes. He was a quiet-looking man, not much taller than she was, but with a quality of toughness and restraint that was oddly unsettling. Once, they had been lovers, Rosalind thought sadly. Now she couldn't think of anything to say to him.

'Did you have a good flight?' It was the best she could do.

'Actually, no,' said Michael, abruptly losing patience. 'It was long and late and extremely uncomfortable, and I've had to leave the site at the worst possible time, so I'm in no mood for small talk. Why don't you stop pretending that we're polite strangers and say what you've got to say?'

'We *are* strangers now.' Rosalind glanced at him and then away. She should never have let Emma talk her into this, she realised, turning her engagement ring in an unconsciously nervous gesture. It was hopeless trying to talk to him. Too much lay between them. 'You've changed,' she said sadly.

'You haven't,' Michael told her in a hard voice. 'Come on, Rosalind, you may as well tell me what it is you want. And I presume you *do* want something? You always did.'

Rosalind winced inwardly at his tone, but she put her chin up and turned back to look him straight in the eye.

She didn't feel much like small talk either. 'All right,' she admitted. 'I do want something.'

'And what is it you want this time? Someone to come running whenever you crook your little finger? Or just someone who'll lie down and turn himself into a doormat so that you can walk all over him?'

He hadn't forgiven her, Rosalind realised bleakly. He could have no idea how bitterly she regretted treating him the way she had, but surely he must have seen by now that they would have been a disaster together? There was no point in arguing, though. She couldn't afford to get involved in the past. It was the present that mattered now...and Jamie.

'It's nothing like that,' she made herself say evenly. 'I need your help. It's important.'

'Everything was always important to you, I seem to remember,' said Michael. 'People spend their whole time helping you. If you can't manipulate them into doing what you want, you simply buy them. Has it ever occurred to you, Rosalind, that if you lifted one of those perfectly manicured fingers you could help *yourself?*'

Rosalind flushed and curled her fingers in her lap. 'This is different,' she said grittily.

Rubbing a hand over his face in a gesture of weary resignation, Michael moved away from the window at last and slumped down opposite her in an armchair. 'So what exactly is it that you want that's so different?' he asked.

He looked tired, Rosalind noticed with sudden compunction. He had been travelling for two days and obviously she was the last person he had wanted to see at the end of his journey. Perhaps she should just leave it?

And then what? Carry on as she was, just hoping that the problem would go away? The prospect chilled her.

She couldn't cope with that any more. She was tired too: tired of looking over her shoulder, tired of tensing every time the phone rang or the door opened, tired of worrying where Jamie was and who he was with as soon as he was out of her sight. She didn't want to ask for Michael's help any more than he wanted to give it, but for Jamie's sake she had to.

Unconsciously squaring her shoulders, she looked straight at Michael. 'Emma says that you're on your way to Yorkshire to visit a great-aunt you haven't seen for years.'

Michael returned her gaze warily. 'What is it to you?'

'I want you to take me with you.'

There was a long, splintering silence. 'You want *what?*'

Rosalind took a deep, steadying breath. She had started, and now she would have to finish. 'It's not just me. There'll be Jamie as well.'

The light grey gaze surveyed her in disbelief, patently searching for some evidence that she was joking. Rosalind wondered which idea he found most bizarre, that she should want to go with him anywhere, let alone to see an old aunt in Yorkshire, or that she should think that he would be prepared to take her?

'And who exactly is Jamie?' he asked in a dangerously quiet voice.

'Jamie is my brother.'

It was obviously the last thing he had expected. 'Your *brother?*' Michael frowned. 'I didn't know you had a brother.'

'He's my half-brother really.' Rosalind forced herself to meet his eyes. 'My father married again after…after you went overseas.'

After you asked me to marry you and I threw your

proposal in your face, she amended wearily to herself. That was what she should have said. She could tell from the expression on Michael's face that he was thinking exactly the same thing, and her gaze slid away from his.

'Daddy was killed last November,' she went on. 'You probably read about it in the newspapers.' Gerald Leigh had been famous as much for his flamboyant style as his global business interests, and for a time his unexpected death had made international news.

Michael nodded briefly.

'Natasha—his wife—was with him when the helicopter went down,' Rosalind made herself go on. 'They were on their way back to Jamie's birthday party. He was three.'

She looked down at her hands as she remembered that cold November day. She had been out shopping when her mobile phone had rung. 'I don't think Jamie really understood. He had his nanny, so outwardly life didn't change that much for him.' It had been different for her. One phone call, and her whole life had turned upside down.

Wondering whether she would be able to explain how she had felt, Rosalind glanced at Michael to find that he was watching her with something that might almost have been understanding, but as their eyes met his expression shuttered and he looked abruptly away. 'Look, I'm sorry about your father, of course,' he said tersely, 'but what has this got to do with me?'

Obscurely hurt by the way he had turned away, Rosalind put up her chin. 'I'm coming to that,' she said.

Ignoring Michael's impatience, she paused to gather her thoughts into the right order. 'As next of kin, I suddenly found myself guardian to Jamie. Natasha and I never really got on, so I'd hardly spent any time with him, and I didn't think then that I would have to change my life that much. I did move back into the Belgravia house, but I thought all I would really have to do would be to make sure he had a nanny to look after him.'

'Being responsible for a child involves a bit more than appointing a nanny!' said Michael, not even bothering to hide his contempt. 'You can't just hand it over to a fleet of servants just because it takes up some of your shopping time!'

'So I've discovered.' Rosalind kept her voice even with an effort. She needed Michael, she reminded herself with an edge of desperation. She couldn't afford to let his sarcasm and obvious dislike rile her. 'If you'd let me finish, I was about to say that it didn't take me long to realise that I'd been wrong. Jamie's part of my life now, and he's very important to me. I wouldn't be here if it wasn't for him.'

'All right, so you're looking after your brother,' sighed Michael, unimpressed. 'You still haven't explained *why* you want to go to Yorkshire or why I'm suddenly expected to act as chauffeur!'

'Jamie's in danger.' Rosalind had rather hoped that her bald statement would shock him, but she should have known better. Instead of starting up in horror, or catching her sustainingly in his arms with promises to protect her, he just looked profoundly irritated.

'What sort of danger?'

'I don't know exactly,' Rosalind said slowly, 'but I'm afraid.'

She saw Michael begin to make a gesture of impatience and leant forward to interrupt him before he could say anything annihilating. 'Please,' she said, 'can I just tell you about it?' Her green eyes pleaded with him. 'I've never had to beg for anything before,' she went on, with an honesty that seemed to startle him, 'but I'm begging now. Let me explain.'

Their eyes met for an airless moment before Michael seemed to make an effort to jerk his away as he raked his fingers through his hair. 'Oh, very well,' he said, half-irritable, half-resigned.

It wasn't the sympathetic reaction she had hoped for, but at least he was listening. 'I've been getting anonymous letters and phone calls,' said Rosalind starkly. 'They started after my father died. At first I thought it was just a crank, someone who'd seen my picture in a magazine or something. They weren't even particularly threatening, just somebody wanting me to know that they'd seen me and that they knew where I'd been and what I'd been wearing. I thought it was creepy, but no more than that, and I chucked the letters away.'

Just talking about it was making her feel tense. Restlessly, Rosalind got to her feet and walked over to the fireplace, as if she wanted to get warm, although there was no fire lit. She hugged her arms together instead and turned back to Michael.

'Then the phone calls started. I can't tell you what the voice is like…' She shivered, remembering the malevolence hissing down the phone. 'I don't even know if it's a man or a woman. What's really frightened me is that he—or she, I suppose—has started to talk about Jamie. He keeps saying things like, "That was a nice blue coat Jamie was wearing today, wasn't it?" so that I know he's watching us.'

Hearing her voice beginning to tremble, Rosalind took another steadying breath. She wasn't going to dissolve into tears and give Michael an excuse to accuse her of being hysterical. 'And now he's making threats about him. "It would be awful if Jamie got lost, wouldn't it?"

''You wouldn't want anyone to hurt him, would you?''...that kind of thing.' She swallowed and clutched her arms closer together. 'I put the phone down, of course, but I'm terrified this...this *creep*...is planning to try and kidnap Jamie.'

'Has anybody ever tried to approach you outside?'

She shook her head. 'I've never seen anyone, but I know he's watching us wherever we go.'

'It sounds very unpleasant,' said Michael after a moment, 'but surely it's a matter for the police?'

'I've spoken to them,' said Rosalind with a trace of impatience. 'They're doing what they can, but there's a limit to what they can do when it's just a question of phone calls and letters, and it's not even as if there have been any specific threats made. My number's unlisted, but I changed it anyway, and it hasn't made any difference.'

Michael frowned, as if annoyed with himself for getting involved in her story. 'Why not just go away for a while?' he found himself suggesting. 'It's not as if you can't afford it.'

'Do you think I haven't thought of that? I took Jamie and his nanny to see his grandmother in Los Angeles in February. It was wonderful for the first three days, and then a letter arrived, hand-delivered.' Rosalind's mouth twisted at the memory. She had just allowed herself to relax when the maid had brought her the letter which had been found in the mailbox.

She looked at Michael, her eyes dark and enormous in her pale face. 'This isn't a stranger, Michael. It's someone who knows me, who knows my friends, who can get on a plane and follow me wherever I go.'

Would he understand her fear? Would he be able to imagine what it was like not to be able to trust anybody?

To spend your whole time when you were out looking from one face to another and wondering: Is it you? Is it you?

As always, though, it was impossible to know what Michael was really thinking. 'What did you do then?' he asked.

Rosalind lifted her hands in a hopeless gesture. 'We came home. At least here we were on familiar territory. Unfortunately the nanny was so spooked by then that she resigned, and I haven't dared to replace her. I can't hand Jamie over to a stranger when there's someone out there who might be prepared to do anything to hurt him.'

'So who's looking after him at the moment?'

'I am,' said Rosalind with a shade of defiance.

Michael didn't say anything. He just looked at her pale green suit with its short skirt and cropped jacket, at the sheer tights, at the heels on her impractical strappy shoes, at the flawless make-up, the immaculately painted nails. He raised one disbelieving brow, and Rosalind coloured.

'I'm not usually dressed like this,' she said, refraining from adding that she had worn the outfit because she knew it suited her and she had wanted to impress him. Not that she needed to have bothered. It took an awful lot, she remembered too late, to impress Michael.

Michael leant back in his chair and linked his hands behind his head, clearly enjoying the sight of Rosalind, flushed and defensive in her elegant outfit by the mantelpiece, and she was suddenly, burningly aware of how she must look to him: more appropriately dressed for a fashion shoot than for looking after a small and very energetic boy. 'I'd like to see you dealing with a grubby toddler,' he said, amused.

'You can,' said Rosalind a little breathlessly. The

amusement gleaming in the grey eyes had transformed him from a distant stranger into the Michael she remembered, the intriguing, inaccessible Michael, with the smile that was as devastating as it was unexpected. Just the thought of that smile was enough to dry the breath in Rosalind's throat, and she wished she hadn't remembered it. It meant remembering other things about him, like the feel of his cool, quiet mouth and his warm hands, and the look in his eyes as he pulled her into his arms…things she would be much better off forgetting.

'I don't think so.'

With a mixture of relief and disappointment, Rosalind saw the smile vanish from Michael's face as he dropped his hands and got abruptly to his feet. 'I'm sure you're waiting for my sympathy, and I don't mind saying that I'm sorry for you if that's what you want, but I don't see what you expect me to do about it, or what you can possibly hope to achieve by coming to Askerby with me. If this person who's harassing you can get himself to Los Angeles, he shouldn't find Yorkshire too much of a problem.'

'That's why I need to disguise myself,' said Rosalind eagerly, seeing an opening at last.

Michael cast her a sardonic glance. 'What were you thinking of? A false nose and a moustache?'

'No, something far simpler than that.'

'Oh, yes?' he mocked. 'So what were you planning to disguise yourself *as*?'

Rosalind took a tiny breath and prayed to keep her voice cool. 'As your wife,' she said.

She could hear her words echoing in the blistering silence: your *wife…wife…wife.* She swallowed. 'And Jamie could be your son.'

'I'm sorry, I think there must be something wrong

with my hearing,' said Michael, pretending to shake his ear. 'Could you say that again? For a minute, there, I thought you were suggesting that you come to Yorkshire with me and pretend to be my wife! Of course, I realised straight away that I must have misheard. Even you, Rosalind, couldn't be arrogant enough to toss aside a proposal of marriage and assume five years later that the man you rejected so casually would still be infatuated enough to agree to take part in a farce like that!'

Rosalind coloured, but gritted her teeth and ploughed on. 'I'm not asking you because of that,' she said. 'I know quite well you're not infatuated with me. I'm asking you because you can offer me the perfect disguise,' she tried to explain. 'This man, woman, whoever it is who's making my life such a misery, is going to be looking for me and Jamie wherever we go. He's *not* going to be looking for the wife and child of a man he's never heard of. That's why it has to be you.'

The words were tumbling out of Rosalind's mouth now, in her haste to convince him. 'This person knows me, he might even know me quite well, but he won't know you. Emma is the only one who knows of any connection between us at all, and I trust her absolutely.'

'Why? Because she's not rich enough to associate with your other friends? I suppose it's the fact that she can't afford to follow you out to America that puts her above suspicion!'

'No,' said Rosalind tightly, beginning to get as angry as Michael. Did he think it had been easy for her to ask him if she could pretend to be his wife, knowing that she had already rejected his genuine offer of marriage? Did he have any *idea* of how humiliating that was? 'It's nothing to do with money. You've never understood our friendship, but Emma and I have been close ever since school, and I dare say I know her better than you do! I trust her absolutely.'

As if on cue, the door opened and Emma came in with a tray laden with a cafetière, three mugs, a plastic beaker, and a plate of biscuits. She held the door open with her hip while an angelic-looking small boy trotted past her. He had fair hair and big brown eyes with ridiculously long lashes, and he clutched a toy train in one hand and a crumbling biscuit in the other.

At the sight of Michael, he stopped dead and stared at him with a child's unnervingly frank gaze. 'This is Jamie,' said Emma as she set down the tray on the coffee table. 'You haven't met him before, have you?'

'No.' Michael made an effort to master his temper and managed a smile. 'Hello, Jamie.'

Jamie regarded him carefully. 'Hello,' he said eventually, having apparently accepted him. 'I've got a train.'

'So I see,' said Michael. 'I used to have one like that when I was a little boy.'

'Look.' Jamie wasn't a very outgoing child, but to Rosalind's surprise he went over to Michael's side and held out his train. Michael crouched down to her little brother's level and inspected the toy gravely, turning it between his long fingers. Rosalind watched Jamie's face as they shared an apparently intent conversation, and felt the by now familiar tightening of her heart. It was hard to believe that she hadn't always loved him.

Her gaze moved on to Michael with a trace of puzzlement. He was such a cool, self-contained person that she hadn't expected him to be good with children, but he seemed to have enslaved Jamie already. Rosalind looked at the two of them together, and something twisted inside her.

'Well?' said Emma in an undertone as she knelt down

by the coffee table to plunge the top of the cafetière. 'Have you sorted everything out yet?'

'Not really,' said Rosalind, forcing her attention back to the problem as she went back to sit on the sofa.

Michael had overheard. He returned the train to Jamie's sticky grasp and left him squatting on the floor, attention divided between his toy and his biscuit. 'We'd got as far as Rosalind suggesting that I saddle myself with a wife and child for my trip to Yorkshire,' he told his sister as he accepted a mug of coffee.

'As you've probably gathered from his tone, Michael doesn't think it's a good idea,' said Rosalind with a sigh.

'But why not?' Emma sat back on her heels and looked at her brother in honest surprise.

Michael sucked in his breath impatiently. 'Actually, I think it *is* a good idea for you to disappear for a few weeks,' he said, with a wintry glance at Rosalind. 'I just don't see why it has to be with me.' He turned to his sister, hoping that she at least would be able to see sense. 'Rosalind can afford to go anywhere in the world,' he pointed out.

'Exactly!' his sister pounced. 'Which is why a quiet Yorkshire village is the last place anyone who wanted to find her would think of looking for her.'

'Fine, let her go to Yorkshire if that's what she wants, but why drag me into it?'

'Oh, Michael, you only have to look at her!' As one, brother and sister turned to study Rosalind, who was looking utterly out of place on the shabby sofa. There was an indefinable gloss about her, an aura of wealth and sophistication that was only partly due to the expensive clothes she wore. It was obvious in the sheen of her lovely hair, in the flawless make-up, in the very way she sat there, taking their attention as her due.

'She'd stand out a mile wherever she went,' Emma pointed out unnecessarily. 'Roz isn't the kind of girl who doesn't get noticed. She may not be exactly a celebrity, but plenty of people know her name, or would recognise her picture from the gossip columns. If she and Jamie go as themselves, it wouldn't take any time for someone to track her down. They have to have a new identity, just for a few weeks, until the police can trace whoever's doing this to her.

'It was actually the police themselves who suggested it,' Emma went on to her brother. 'And that's when I thought of you. I'd just had your message saying that you were coming back for a month to sort out Aunt Maud, and I suddenly realised that you would be perfect cover. Nobody associates you with Rosalind, and, more importantly, you're going somewhere where nobody knows you or expects you to be anything other than who you say you are. If you introduce Rosalind and Jamie as your wife and son, who's going to question it?'

'Aunt Maud?' Michael suggested acidly, but Emma waved their great-aunt aside.

'She hasn't been in touch with the family for over twenty years, so she isn't to know whether you're married or not, is she?'

'Maybe not,' he said with one of his implacable looks, 'but she's an old lady, and she sounds confused and in need of help. I don't see why she should have a strange woman and a small child foisted on her under false pretences.'

'Oh, Michael!' cried Emma in disappointment. 'You *can't* refuse! Rosalind and Jamie are in danger, and you're the only one who can help them!'

Michael's mouth tightened. 'That's nonsense, Emma, and you know it.' He looked at Rosalind, who was sitting on the sofa, unconsciously twisting a spectacular band of diamonds around the third finger of her left hand and wondering how she was going to be able to protect Jamie now. 'You don't need to keep fiddling with that ring,' he told her roughly. 'I got the message that you'd found someone good enough for you as soon as I saw how ostentatious it was!'

Emma was looking puzzled at Michael's tone, and Rosalind hurried into speech before her friend could realise that her relationship with Michael had been rather more than that of his sister's schoolfriend. She hadn't wanted to talk about what had happened five years ago, and obviously neither had Michael.

'I wasn't trying to give you any *message*,' she said to him with a frosty look. 'I twist the ring round my finger when I'm thinking, that's all.'

'But it *is* an engagement ring?'

Rosalind hesitated fractionally. She should have thought to take the ring off before she came. Her engagement just complicated matters. 'Yes, it is.'

'In that case I suggest you ask whoever gave it to you to take you away,' said Michael in a flat voice.

'I can't.' Rosalind bit her lip. She didn't really want to talk about Simon, whose flat refusal to get involved in the whole affair hurt more than she cared to admit.

'Can't? Why not?' Michael nodded at the ring, winking in the light on Rosalind's hand. 'Surely anyone who's prepared to fork out for a bit of jewellery like that should care enough to traipse up and down the country with you, if that's what you want?'

'It's not as easy as that,' Rosalind protested.

'Roz is engaged to Simon Hungerford,' Emma explained after a moment. 'You must have heard of him.'

'Hungerford?' Michael thought. 'The politician?'

'That's right,' said Emma.

Michael's eyes travelled to Rosalind's suddenly hot face. 'You and Simon Hungerford?' he said slowly. 'Yes, it makes sense. Only someone like him would do for you. The Hungerfords are one of the few families that can rival yours for wealth, and I've read that Simon is now pursuing power with the same ruthless ambition that the rest of his family use to pursue money. You and he should be well matched!'

Rosalind flinched at the contempt lacing his voice, but she lifted her chin and did her best to ignore it. 'It's very difficult for Simon to get away.' She tried to excuse him. 'Even if he didn't have all his commitments, he's too well-known. Someone would be bound to recognise him, then we'd have the papers onto us, and we might as well put a notice in the paper telling our stalker where we were!'

'So you see, it has to be you, Michael,' cajoled Emma, offering the plate of biscuits. But Michael was clearly in no mood to be succumb even to his sister's coaxing.

He ignored the biscuits. 'I'm sorry, Emma,' he said uncompromisingly, 'but I've got enough on my plate at the moment without acting as bodyguard. Rosalind's got a fiancé to protect her, and if he's not prepared to look after her himself, he can afford to pay for someone to do it for him. I've got more important things to do.'

CHAPTER TWO

HE HAD said no. He had *meant* no.

So why the hell was he driving up the M1 with Rosalind beside him and Jamie asleep in the back seat? Michael asked himself savagely the next morning.

If it hadn't been for that damned phone call he would have been on his own and concentrating on pushing all the memories of Rosalind firmly back into a box marked 'Big Mistake', where they had lived until she had walked through the door and set them swirling free. Five minutes later, and she would have been gone. He would have been able to get on with his own life. But they had still been drinking coffee when Rosalind's mobile phone had rung.

Michael hadn't paid much attention at first. Jamie had spilt some of his juice on Rosalind's skirt, and she and Emma had been jumping up and down, looking for a cloth, dabbing away at the stain, wiping Jamie's hands. The imperative buzz of the phone had sent Rosalind in a frantic search for her bag, which she turned out to have left on a table by the door.

'That'll be Simon,' she said to Emma, throwing her the cloth. 'He said he would ring about now.'

Irritated by all the fuss, Michael was prowling around the room with his mug and wondering how Rosalind could possibly hope to look after a small boy when she couldn't cope with a bit of spilt juice. Then something in the quality of the silence made him turn, and he put his coffee down on the television so abruptly that it slopped over the edge.

Rosalind was frozen by the door, the phone clamped to her ear, and she was staring straight ahead, an expression of such stark terror in her eyes that the breath stuck in his throat.

Afterwards, he had no memory of crossing the room. One moment he was there by the television, the next he was snatching the phone from Rosalind's nerveless hand. '—shame if anything were to happen to such a pretty little boy, wouldn't it?' he heard, and understood what Rosalind had meant about the voice. It was curiously sexless, and so thick with malevolence that his flesh crawled. 'You see, I know where you are. I know he's with you—'

Michael had heard enough. He cut the connection and put the phone slowly down on the coffee table, his mouth twisted in distaste. Emma was looking appalled, Jamie puzzled and a little anxious, as if he feared that the atmosphere of dread was somehow a consequence of the spilt juice. Rosalind herself was staring blankly ahead, her lips clamped so fiercely together that Michael could practically feel the effort it was costing her not to let them tremble.

Taking her arm, he propelled her back to the sofa and made her sit down. Her slender body was rigid with tension, and, sensing her distress, Jamie leant against her knee. Rosalind put her arm around him and hugged him tightly against her. 'It's all right, sweetheart, there's nothing for you to worry about,' she said a little unsteadily, and then she lifted her eyes and Michael found himself looking straight into their shimmering green depths.

'All right,' he heard himself say. 'You can come to Yorkshire with me tomorrow.'

Why had he said it? It was none of his business, Michael reminded himself. This was Rosalind, the ice queen herself, and if anyone should have learnt to distrust those big green eyes it was him. So why did she just have to look at him like that for him to realise that even after all these years the thought of her being hurt or frightened was unendurable? Michael, sucked into a flurry of arrangements, wasn't sure he wanted to know the answer to that.

At least he had had the sense to lay down some conditions, he thought now, grimly overtaking a car hogging the middle lane. It was obvious that Rosalind hadn't thought beyond persuading him to take her with him, and she had been taken aback when he had told her that she was going to have to do something about the way she looked.

'You're going to have to change your image,' he had told her. 'You'll stick out like a sore thumb in a Yorkshire village, looking the way you do at the moment. No one's going to believe you're an archaeologist's wife if you prance around wearing clothes that probably cost half a year of my salary.'

He had expected her to protest, but it seemed that Rosalind had decided not to push her luck. Her expression, though, when Emma laid out the clothes Michael had sent her to buy, was eloquent.

'Couldn't I take some of my own things?' she pleaded, holding up a brown corduroy skirt and eyeing it with a mixture of disbelief and distaste.

'You can take your own jeans and your own underwear, but anything else you wear in public has got to be from this lot,' said Michael, who was still furious with himself for not walking away while he had the chance and in no mood to compromise.

'But I'll look so frumpy!'

He gritted his teeth. 'That, Rosalind, is the whole point! I told Emma to get you practical clothes that were suitable for an ordinary mother of an ordinary toddler. If you want to blend into the background so that no one will notice you, you're going to have to dress like everyone else.'

Rosalind sighed and dropped the skirt back onto the table, where Emma had spread the clothes after her shopping excursion. 'I thought it would be enough if you just presented me as your wife.'

'Well, it won't,' said Michael. 'If you want to get yourself noticed, turn up looking as you do now. But don't expect me to tell anyone that you're anything to do with me! And it's not just a question of what you wear. While you're at it, you'd better do something about your hair.'

Rosalind's hands went instinctively to her head, to the long, rippling copper tresses that he had once loved. 'What about my hair?'

'Cut it,' Michael said flatly, taking a perverse satisfaction in the thought of her without that glorious, silky, shining hair, 'and then dye it.'

Rosalind eyed him mutinously. 'And if I won't?'

'Then I won't take you with me,' he told her.

'That's blackmail!'

He shrugged, unperturbed. 'It's up to you.'

'He's right, I'm afraid, Roz,' Emma had said apologetically when Rosalind had appealed to her for support. 'Your hair's so beautiful and such an unusual colour that someone would be bound to remark on it. They might even recognise it. Remember all those photos of you and Simon in the papers when your engagement was announced? There were lots of comments about your hair then.'

Michael had been half-hoping that Rosalind would refuse to give in to his ultimatum, and provide him with the excuse he needed to call the whole thing off, but when he'd seen her this morning, her hair had been cut to fall just below her jawline and coloured a dull, mousy brown. From a distance, he had hardly recognised her.

Now, he glanced at her where she sat beside him, staring tensely through the windscreen at the carriageway. With her badly cut brown hair and a bulky blue cotton jumper which she wore over her jeans, she should have looked like a stranger. He had *wanted* her to be a stranger, to keep the bitter memories away, but it wasn't as easy as that. Nothing could change the achingly pure lines of her profile, or the sweep of lashes over the lustrous green eyes.

She was still the same Rosalind. The same elusive, alluring, bitterly familiar fragrance hung gossamer-light in the air between them. The same curve of her mouth, the same enticing hollow at the base of her throat. The same ability to make his throat tighten every time he looked at her.

Michael's hands gripped the steering wheel. The same selfishness, he reminded himself with an edge of desperation. The same vanity. The same arrogance.

Beside him, Rosalind turned for the umpteenth time to check on Jamie. He was sleeping, strapped into the child seat that Michael had hired with the car, his golden head lolling to one side and the impossibly long lashes lying against his downy cheeks, and, as always now, she was conscious of a fierce upsurge of protective tenderness. He was safe; that was all that mattered. It was worth losing her hair, worth every one of the dreary outfits filling her case, even worth putting up with Michael's hostility.

She still wasn't sure what had made him change his mind. There had been a moment after that awful phone call when she could have sworn that she saw concern for her in his eyes, but if so he wasn't admitting to it. He had been brusque with her ever since, and when she had tried to thank him he had just brushed her gratitude aside.

'I'm doing this for Jamie, not for you,' he had told her, and she had looked straight into the shuttered grey gaze.

'So am I,' she had said.

With a sigh, Rosalind turned back to face forwards, and lifted a surreptitious hand to the nape of her neck. It felt very strange without the heavy curtain of hair falling down her back. Released from its own weight, her hair had sprung up, and now waved softly around her face. She kept shaking her head to feel its lightness. The long, thick mass of hair had been part of her for so long that she felt vulnerable and yet curiously liberated without it.

'Stop fiddling with your hair,' said Michael irritably.

'I can't help it,' she protested. 'I don't feel like me at all.'

'You wanted a disguise,' he pointed out.

'I know,' said Rosalind, turning to look out of her window. 'I just didn't realise that looking different would make me *feel* so different.'

'I hope it's going to make you behave differently,' he said, without taking his eyes off the road.

She sent him a glance of resentment and then looked pointedly back out of the side window. 'I didn't realise archaeologists' wives behaved any differently from the rest of us!'

'The *rest of us*?' Michael lifted a caustic brow. 'How many women do you think behave like you?'

'Plenty, I should think,' retorted Rosalind, beginning to get cross. 'I may have more money than most, but it doesn't mean that I don't think and feel just like anyone else.'

'You certainly don't behave like the kind of woman I'd be likely to marry,' he said, with a sideways glance of dislike.

Provoked, she swung back round in her seat to face him, green eyes narrowed dangerously. 'You would have married me once if I'd accepted you,' she reminded him in a silky voice. 'Or had you forgotten?'

There was a tiny pause. 'No, I hadn't forgotten,' he said evenly. 'But I'd be looking for something more in a wife than mere beauty now.'

'Such as?'

'Love,' said Michael. 'But of course you wouldn't understand about that, would you, Rosalind? Love was never part of your agenda.'

His voice was cold with dislike, and Rosalind dug her fingernails into her palms, determined not to let him know that he had hurt her. 'Perhaps it's just as well I didn't marry you, then,' she said with a brittle smile.

'Perhaps it is,' he agreed.

'I hope you're duly grateful to me for refusing you?'

'I wouldn't say that I felt particularly grateful at the time,' he said tonelessly, 'but you were certainly right in thinking that we weren't suited.'

Rosalind knew that she had been right, but somehow it hadn't been much comfort after Michael had left, and somehow it still wasn't. The brief, invigorating spurt of anger had faded as quickly as it had arisen, leaving her tired and inexplicably depressed.

'That must be the first time you've ever agreed with me about anything.' She had meant it to sound like a joke, but instead she sounded merely sad.

'Is it?'

There was an odd note in his voice, and Rosalind wondered if he, too, was thinking about the times when they had argued and fought and then kissed and made up. In bed, at least, they had always agreed. She could still feel the shivery delight of his mouth against her skin, of his slow, sure hands exploring her body.

Silence, jangling with memories, stretched between them. Rosalind found herself remembering Emma's twenty-first birthday party. She had worn a sea-green dress that showed off her long legs and an expanse of smooth, golden back, and she had been laughing as someone refilled her glass with champagne when her gaze had caught Michael's across the room. His eyes had been light and peculiarly alive in his austere face, and Rosalind, oddly jolted, had jerked her gaze away and taken a gulp of champagne.

When she'd glanced up again, he had gone. Half irritated by her own interest, Rosalind had circulated, scanning the party in the hope of seeing him again, but he seemed to have disappeared. And then, just when she had given up, Emma had dragged her aside to introduce her to her brother.

'This is Michael,' she had said, and Rosalind had looked into the same cool, grey eyes and felt her heart lurch.

If Michael had recognised her from the brief, burning glance they had exchanged, he'd given no sign of it. He'd been polite but unimpressed, and Rosalind, who had learnt to accept universal and uncritical admiration as her due, had been piqued. There had been a faint air of disapproval about him, an undercurrent of mockery in his voice, that had put her on her mettle. Who was Michael Brooke to disapprove of *her*? He wasn't handsome; he wasn't charming. He was just the brother of a schoolfriend. So why did she find him so intriguing?

Of course, their relationship had been doomed from the start. Michael hadn't belonged in her smart, superficial, social world; she'd been an alien, exotic creature in his. When it had come down to it, they had had absolutely nothing in common. And yet...Rosalind couldn't help remembering how the differences between them had dissolved the moment they touched. Five years on, she could still feel the frisson of excitement that had shuddered down her spine if Michael so much as brushed her skin with his fingers.

Almost against her will, her gaze slid sidewards to rest on his hands, controlled and competent on the steering wheel, and memory churned inside her at the thought of those same hands drifting possessively over her body, melting her bones with their hard promise, slowly—

Rosalind wrenched her eyes away, only to find herself looking at Michael's mouth instead, and the breath snarled in her throat. Now, it was compressed into a grim line, but she knew just how it could relax into a rare, unexpected smile that had never failed to leave her dizzy with pleasure, as if she had been given a wonderful present out of the blue. And those lips, set so implacably now, had once lingered tantalisingly against her skin, corners curving upwards as he felt her shiver in delight.

Drawing an uneven breath, Rosalind forced herself to look away. She stared desperately at the number plate of the car ahead of them, reading it over and over again, as if by memorising it she could wipe out all those other memories.

It was stupid to feel so edgy. Other couples broke up and managed to meet again without this excruciating tension. Rosalind wriggled her shoulders against the seat-back and made herself relax. They might not be able to forget the past, but at least they could pretend.

'Did you get a chance to ring your aunt?' she asked, in an effort to ease the atmosphere.

Michael nodded, but didn't look at her. 'I told her that I'd be a little later than expected, and that I'd be bringing my wife and son with me.' There was a faintly distasteful emphasis when he mentioned her assumed role, but Rosalind soldiered on, determined to keep the conversation as neutral as possible.

'Did she mind?'

He shrugged. 'It was hard to tell. Her telephone manner was brusque, to say the least, but she might be like that all the time.'

'Emma says that she's rather eccentric.' Rosalind settled more comfortably in her seat, oddly encouraged by the fact that Michael was actually talking to her at last.

'So we've always been told, but neither of us know very much about her. I haven't seen Aunt Maud since I was nine. I remember being taken to tea. She was a bit intimidating, but I liked her in a funny sort of way. She talked to us children exactly as she did to the adults.'

Rosalind was doing some mental calculations. 'But if you were nine when you last met, that means it's over twenty years since you've seen her!'

'Twenty-two,' Michael agreed. 'Maud was married to my grandfather's brother, and there was some kind of rift with my grandmother. I don't know what it was about—probably something quite trivial—but words were said and offence taken on both sides, and Aunt Maud broke off all contact with the family. My great-uncle died about five or six years ago, and I have to admit that I assumed that she was dead too until I got a letter from her out of the blue a couple of months back.'

'A letter? What did it say?'

'Just that she couldn't cope with looking after my great-uncle's affairs any longer, and practically ordering me as the last man of the family to go up and take responsibility for them.'

Rosalind stole another glance at him. His Aunt Maud was a braver woman than she knew. 'It's not like you to let yourself be ordered around,' she commented, and was rewarded with a smile. It was just a small one, hardly a smile at all, more a twitch of the lips and a dent at the corner of his mouth, but Rosalind felt as if she'd scaled a mountain and she hugged her achievement to her.

'I can't say I liked it,' Michael acknowledged ruefully, unaware of the effect his almost-smile had had on Rosalind. 'My first impulse was to write back and tell her to get herself a good solicitor, but her letter bothered me. Reading between the lines, it seemed to me that she was asking for help, but too proud to beg for it. She's an old lady now; she's got no children and she's all on her own.'

He paused as he slipped into the fast lane to overtake three trucks trundling nose to tail. 'I got the impression that the business was just an excuse to rebuild some bridges, so I wrote back and explained that I was overseas, but that I would go and see her next time I had some leave. This is the first opportunity I've had to get away.'

'So you've come all the way back to the UK for the

sake of an old aunt you haven't seen for twenty-two years?'

'Emma and I are the only family she's got,' said Michael, faintly defensive, 'and since our father died I suppose she's the only family we've got too. I can't just ignore her.'

'No.' She glanced over her shoulder at Jamie, still sleeping peacefully. 'No, I know what you mean. I thought I could ignore Jamie, but when it came down to it, I couldn't.'

He shot her a look of disbelief. 'Why would you want to ignore your own brother?'

Rosalind didn't answer immediately. She clasped her hands together in her lap and looked down at her linked fingers. 'I suppose I was jealous,' she said slowly. 'I know it's an awful thing to say. I didn't like Natasha, and she didn't like me, and when she and my father got married I felt so excluded that I moved out and bought my own place. It was even worse when Jamie was born.' Her voice was light and self-mocking, but Michael sensed the suppressed hurt behind her words. 'I was used to being Daddy's only little girl, and suddenly there was a baby...'

'And a boy? No wonder your nose was out of joint!'

'Yes, that's how it felt.' A flush stained Rosalind's cheekbones. 'I'm not very proud of myself. Daddy was thrilled to have a son.' Her lower lip wavered and she bit down on it. 'I should have been pleased for him. I wish I had been,' she went on in a low voice. 'I wish he could see me with Jamie now.'

Michael checked his mirror and slid the car smoothly back out into the fast lane. 'Is that why you're going to so much trouble for Jamie now? Because you feel guilty?'

'No.' She looked straight ahead. 'I'm doing it because of what Jamie means to me. Everything's been so *complicated* since my father died,' she tried to explain. 'His business affairs were incredibly complex, and there have been endless hassles trying to sort everything out. I inherited controlling shares in a whole raft of companies I know nothing about, and every day I'm asked to authorise documents and agree with decisions which mean nothing to me.

'At first, Jamie was just something else to think about,' Rosalind went on. 'Just somebody else needing decisions to be made about him. And then one day I walked up to see his nanny about her salary and I saw Jamie sitting in the middle of the nursery floor. He wasn't doing anything, he was just sitting there, holding a teddy, but he looked so small and so lonely.'

Her eyes rested on the rear windscreen of the car in front, but she was seeing herself walking up the stairs, glancing through the door and stopping dead as she was gripped by a tenderness that was as terrifying and intense as it was unexpected. Rosalind had learnt early on that love couldn't be trusted, and she'd thought that she was armoured against it, yet in the end all it had taken was the sight of a small boy clutching his teddy to pierce all her defences.

'He reminded me of me,' she said in a low voice, and Michael looked at her sharply.

'Of you?'

'I know what it's like to grow up without a mother,' said Rosalind quietly. 'I spent a lot of my childhood sitting in that nursery while an endless succession of nannies talked about how much they had to be paid for looking after me. When I saw Jamie that day, it was as if I'd never seen him before. I suddenly realised that he was my brother and that he only had me to look after him.'

She swallowed. 'I wanted to explain, to tell him why I hadn't loved him before and to promise that I'd make up for all the lonely days he'd sat there, but I couldn't. He was only three, he wouldn't have understood.'

'I thought you didn't believe in love,' said Michael harshly.

That was what she had told him. Rosalind could hear her careless words echoing down the years and she shifted uneasily in her seat, remembering the expression on Michael's face.

'I didn't,' she said in a flat voice. 'I still don't.'

'You love Jamie,' Michael pointed out, and she glanced at him curiously. There had been a strange undercurrent to his voice that in anyone else might have sounded almost like jealousy.

But what was she thinking of? Rosalind scolded herself. Michael had got over her a long time ago, and he wasn't going to waste his time feeling jealous about her feelings for anyone, least of all a three-year-old boy!

'Sometimes I wish I didn't,' she admitted with a tiny sigh. 'It's terrifying having to think about him the whole time.'

'I can see that thinking about someone else must have been a shock for you,' said Michael, with one of his sardonic looks, but Rosalind ignored it.

'It's not that. It's having to think about looking after him properly. You have to be so careful with children. You have to feed them the right way, bathe them the right way, teach them how to behave the right way... Maybe it comes naturally if you have a baby of your own, but I've never had anything to do with children and I didn't know where to begin.'

Michael was clearly unimpressed. 'Surely it's just a matter of common sense?' he said dismissively.

'Whatever it is, I'm no good at it,' said Rosalind glumly. 'Emma laughs at me, but I went out and bought a book on childcare. I'm so nervous about doing the wrong thing that if Jamie so much as sneezes I rush off and check the section on blowing noses.' She glanced at Michael a little defiantly. 'It's pathetic, isn't it?'

Michael gave her rather an odd look, and Rosalind suddenly wished that she hadn't told him so much. She might not like the idea of him remembering her as a beautiful, heartless bitch, but it was better than him thinking of her as muddling hopelessly along like the rest of the world. At least before she had been different, Rosalind thought, a little dispirited. She had used to think that she could do anything she wanted, but Jamie had taught her that she couldn't. She might have learnt to accept that she could be wrong, or incompetent or afraid, but that didn't mean she had to tell Michael, did it? Where was her pride when she needed it?

She waited for Michael to jeer at her ignorance, but he was frowning through the windscreen. 'Hasn't Jamie got any other relatives with more experience of bringing up children who could help you?' was all he said.

'Natasha's mother lives in Los Angeles. She came over for the funeral and suggested that she take Jamie back with her, but she's always so busy socialising that I know she would just hand him over to a nanny.' Rosalind's mouth hardened. 'I'm not going to let Jamie grow up the way I did.'

'I thought you were the little girl who had everything?' said Michael.

'Except a mother,' said Rosalind. She looked out of her window. 'She left when I was four.'

'She *left* you?' Michael jerked his head round briefly. He sounded shocked. 'Why?'

'She was an actress.' Rosalind kept her voice deliberately light. 'Not a particularly good one, but she was so beautiful it didn't matter. When she got an offer to go to Hollywood, she was convinced she was going to be a big star. But a husband and a small child weren't good for her image, so she just left.'

There was a pause. 'Why didn't you tell me about your mother when we knew each other before?' said Michael eventually, and she shrugged.

'I suppose we had better things to talk about. Anyway, it wasn't a big tragedy by then. I had my father. He was working most of the time, so I didn't see that much of him, but at least I knew he was there. Jamie doesn't even have that.' Rosalind looked at Michael almost fiercely. 'He's not going to be handed over to a series of nannies and produced on high days and holidays,' she told him with a determined lift of her chin. 'I can't be his mother, but I can make sure that I'm there for him for as long as he needs me.'

'And where does Simon Hungerford fit into all this?' asked Michael. 'Is his role to be a father figure for Jamie?'

Rosalind hesitated slightly. Simon had little interest in Jamie, and indeed had a hard time even remembering his name. Most of the time he referred to him as 'the boy'. She was hoping that he would change his mind when he got to know Jamie, as she had done. 'I hope so.'

'Is that why you're marrying him?' The words sounded as if they had been forced out of Michael, and she looked at him for a moment before turning her head away.

'It's one of the reasons.'

'What are the others?' he asked abrasively.

Rosalind didn't answer immediately. She was wondering what he would say if she told him that she had given up hoping to find another man who would make her feel the way he had, and had decided to settle for second best.

'We understand each other,' she said eventually, reminding herself of all the reasons it made sense to marry Simon. 'Simon comes from the same kind of background as I do. We like doing the same things.' She lifted her shoulders in a small, helpless gesture. 'We'll make a good team.'

'No wonder you wouldn't marry me.' There was a bitter edge to Michael's voice. 'You couldn't have said any of those things about us, could you?'

'No.' Rosalind clutched her hands together in her lap and hoped that she sounded calm. 'You and I didn't have anything in common.'

Except the fire that had leapt between them whenever they had touched. Except the laughter as he had pulled her down onto the bed after an argument. Except the brief, intense joy that they had discovered in each other.

'And of course you and Simon do,' said Michael mockingly. 'I might have known you'd hold out for someone from the *right background.* Only someone as rich as Simon Hungerford could be good enough for you!'

'It's not about money,' Rosalind protested.

'Isn't it? Does Simon know that you don't believe in love?'

Rosalind's fingers were gripped so tightly together that her knuckles stood out, taut and white. She looked down at them as Michael's question rang around the car, and wondered why her engagement, which had made such perfect sense, should suddenly seem so sad. And why she cared what Michael thought about it.

'He knows I don't love him,' she said steadily at last.

'Does he love you?'

'No.' Rosalind drew a breath. 'No, he doesn't, but he respects me. We get on well. We're...comfortable together.'

'Comfortable?' Michael laughed. 'What happened to you, Rosalind?' he asked mockingly. 'You used to be so passionate. I always thought of you as the original wild child, and now it turns out all you really wanted was a cup of cocoa and a pair of slippers!'

Rosalind's lips tightened. 'Perhaps I've grown up,' she said in a cold voice.

'Grown up? It sounds as if you've jumped straight from adolescence to old age!'

She glared at him, forgetting her wistfulness in gathering anger at his mockery of her relationship with Simon. 'At least I've outgrown the stage when I was stupid enough to get involved with someone like you!' she snapped. 'Passion's all very well, but it doesn't last.'

'No,' Michael agreed flatly. 'You taught me that.'

'You know it would never have lasted.' There was a defensive note in Rosalind's voice as she shook back her hair, wishing that they had never started this conversation. 'We were both too young, for a start. I never wanted to get involved in an intense relationship like that. I just wanted to have some fun. I thought you understood that was all I was prepared to offer.'

'Obviously I didn't know you as well as Simon does,' said Michael with an edge. 'Does he get to have *fun* as well as all that respect and getting on and being comfortable together?'

Rosalind scowled at his sarcasm. 'That's none of your business!'

CHAPTER THREE

'So,' said Michael after a pause, 'have you told him about us?'

'No,' said Rosalind, still cross. Her chin was tilted at a combative angle as she looked back at him. 'There's nothing to tell. Simon's not interested in any quick flings I might have had when I was younger,' she went on deliberately, in an effort to get her own back. 'It was only a fleeting sexual attraction after all. My relationship with Simon is quite different.'

'It must be.' Michael bared his teeth in an unpleasant smile. 'We may just have had a *fling,* but I would have dropped everything to protect you if you were in the kind of danger you're in now! Simon seems quite happy to stay at home and let someone else do his dirty work for him!'

A hint of colour stained Rosalind's cheekbones. She wasn't about to admit to Michael how Simon's dismissal of her fears had hurt.

'I've explained that. Simon can protect me best by not drawing attention to me.'

'How does he feel about you going off to spend a month as the wife of another man?'

'He understands why it's necessary,' said Rosalind loftily, closing her mind to her last conversation with Simon, who had been horrified at the idea in case the newspapers got hold of the fact that she was effectively living with another man. Rosalind, he felt, should simply stay in London and let the police sort things out. But when she had insisted he had reluctantly agreed, begging her not to cause a scandal as he put down the phone. 'He knows he doesn't need to be jealous of *you,*' she added nastily.

'Of course not,' Michael agreed equally unpleasantly. 'My bank balance isn't big enough to tempt you, is it, Rosalind?'

'Let's just say that you're not my type,' said Rosalind tightly, perversely determined not to let him know that he had hurt her. Why did no one ever understand that money was the last thing she was interested in? She had plenty of her own, and sometimes she hated it. How many times now had she lowered her defences, and let herself believe that someone might be interested in her for her own sake, only to discover that she was apparently nowhere near as interesting as her fortune?

At least she had succeeded in nettling Michael. 'I may not be your type, Rosalind,' he said, 'but at least I'm here. That's more than can be said for your precious fiancé!'

'I might say the same about yours!' snapped Rosalind before she could help herself.

'Mine?' said Michael blankly.

'Emma said that you were thinking of getting married,' she admitted a little sullenly, hoping that he wouldn't guess with what studied casualness she had pumped his sister for news of him over the last five years.

'When did she tell you this?'

'After she went out to visit you in the Middle East last year.'

Rosalind didn't add how inexplicably shaken she had been by the news. Emma hadn't known about the affair between her brother and her best friend. She had gone off to spend the summer in France after the fatal twenty-first birthday party. Afterwards Rosalind hadn't wanted to tell her how much she had hurt Michael, and had been shamefacedly relieved that Michael had apparently told his sister nothing either. So Emma had no way of knowing that her enthusiasm for Michael's girlfriend was like a knife turning in the heart Rosalind had tried so hard to freeze since Michael had gone.

Kathy, it appeared, was pretty and sensible and good fun. 'I wouldn't be surprised if Michael asked her to marry him,' Emma had finished happily. 'He's been waiting for the right woman for years, and now I'm sure he's found her.'

Not that Michael's happiness had had anything to do with Rosalind's decision to accept Simon's long-standing proposal the next week. That had been mere coincidence, she told herself, nothing more.

There was an odd look on Michael's face and Rosalind's gaze sharpened. 'Isn't it true?' she asked, appalled to discover a flicker of hope in her heart. What did it matter to her whether he was engaged or not?

'We're not exactly engaged,' he said, after the most fractional of pauses. 'Kathy doesn't see any reason to formalise our relationship, and neither do I. We're happy as we are.'

'So happy that she's prepared to let you go off without her for a month?'

Michael shrugged. 'Why not? Kathy's got her own work to do.'

'Does she know that you're spending the next month with an ex-lover?'

'No,' he admitted, 'but if she did, it wouldn't bother her. She's heard enough about you to know that you're the last person she need ever be jealous of!'

Rosalind slewed round in her seat to stare at him. 'Do you mean that you've discussed me with her?' she demanded, affronted.

'I met Kathy not long after I went out to the Middle East,' said Michael calmly. 'I was still feeling pretty raw about you. Having a girl laugh in your face at a genuine proposal of marriage doesn't do much for a man's self-esteem. I was hurt and angry and humiliated, and Kathy was just what I needed.'

'It obviously didn't take you long to console yourself anyway,' Rosalind snapped, unwilling to admit even to herself how the thought of Michael finding happiness with another woman grated on her. 'You can't have been that much in love with me if you replaced me that quickly!'

'I wasn't in love with you,' said Michael, and for some reason Rosalind's heart dropped like a stone.

'You—you said you were,' she stammered.

'I know I did, but it was just infatuation.' Calmly, Michael checked his mirrors, flicked the indicator on and pulled into the outside lane to overtake. 'Not surprising, really,' he went on judiciously. 'I was young and you were very beautiful. It would have been amazing if I hadn't been infatuated with you. But luckily I got over it.' Pausing, he glanced sideways at Rosalind, who was staring at him, her face a study of conflicting emotions. 'You didn't believe in love, but Kathy did, and she taught me what it was all about.'

'She sounds perfect.' Rosalind bit out the words, torn between anger, regret and a bitter, hollow feeling that she refused to admit was jealousy.

'She is,' said Michael.

They stopped for lunch at a service station. Michael was glad to get out of the car. Rosalind had sat in simmering silence and he hadn't seen any reason why he should make polite conversation just to ease an atmosphere that she had created. It wasn't him who had insisted on talking about the past.

She hadn't liked him telling her about Kathy, he thought with some satisfaction. The green eyes had looked distinctly stormy. Perhaps it was stupid to have lied, but Michael hadn't been able to resist when Rosalind had let slip that she thought he was engaged. If it hadn't been for the complacent note in her voice when he'd hesitated and she'd asked him if it was true, he might even have told her the truth. As it was, the suspicion that she was waiting to be told that he had never been able to consider marrying anyone except her had grated on Michael's nerves. The fact that it was true was one Michael was damned if he was going to admit, not even to himself, and least of all to Rosalind!

No, let her believe that he was committed to Kathy. Rosalind might not want him, but that didn't mean that no one else would, and it wouldn't do her any harm at all to realise it. Kathy was a nice girl, and he liked her very much, but when she had gone back to her university in the States, he had made no attempt to persuade her to stay.

Still, there was no need to tell Rosalind that.

'Lunch,' he said roughly as he switched off the engine and unclipped his seat belt.

He opened his door and got out. Turning to close it, he saw that Rosalind hadn't moved. She was still sitting there with her hands clutched together, and the tautness of her face hit Michael with the force of a blow. For the first time he noticed the shadows around the huge eyes and the strained set of her mouth. The last few months couldn't have been easy for her, he realised uncomfortably. Not even Rosalind deserved to lose her father in a tragic accident, take on the responsibility for a small child she didn't even want, and then deal with the creeping horror of being stalked.

'Come on, you'll feel better when you've had something to eat,' he said more gently. 'You don't need to worry. I checked my mirror and there was no one behind us when we turned off the motorway.'

'Are you sure?' The green eyes were beseeching, and Michael saw that the snappy pride that had kept her buoyed up in the isolated safety of the car had vanished at the prospect of stepping out into the world again. She had obviously forgotten about the stalker for a while, but now the busy service station had brought the fear rushing back, and she shrank into her seat as Michael opened her door.

'I'm sure,' he said. 'Look, no one's watching us. As far as anyone here is concerned, we're just another ordinary family in another ordinary car.'

'Yes.' Rosalind unclenched her hands and smoothed them on her jeans. 'Yes. Sorry, I just lost my nerve there for a minute.'

Behind her, Jamie stirred and opened his eyes, and by the time Rosalind had lifted him out of the car and straightened his red trousers and striped top she had regained her old poise.

'Are you all right now?' asked Michael, watching her with brusque concern, and she put up her chin, as if afraid that he was about to write her down as gutless and pathetic.

'I'm fine.'

Jamie was thrilled with the self-service restaurant, and stood on tiptoe to inspect the array of food on offer while

Michael collected a tray. Rosalind was patently less impressed. Michael watched her wrinkling her nose fastidiously and was obscurely grateful to see the old, irritating Rosalind back on form.

There had been moments when she had come dangerously close to slipping under his guard again, when he had been ready to swear that she had changed. The Rosalind he had known would never have been prepared to change her life for a small child, and she certainly wouldn't have admitted to uncertainty about whether she was looking after him properly.

On the other hand, there had been plenty to remind him that she was still the same, Michael reminded himself. Look at her now, turning up her nose at the sandwiches, utterly out of place in spite of her jeans and jumper! She had probably never queued for food in her life before, he realised. Perhaps she hadn't had the easy, pampered childhood that he had always assumed, but it would be as well not to forget that she still belonged in a different stratosphere from him.

As soon as they had paid, Jamie rushed over to choose a table by the window, where he could watch the traffic flashing past. 'Wonderful, a view!' sighed Rosalind as she lowered her tray onto the table.

Usually a picky eater, Jamie gobbled down his sausages and beans, and then knelt up on his seat to press his nose against the window. Rosalind moved his plate out of range of his sleeve. 'If I'd known he was this easy to entertain, I would have brought him to a motorway weeks ago!' she said.

'It's different from what he's used to,' Michael pointed out.

She toyed unenthusiastically with the remains of a

salad. 'It's different from what I'm used to, but I can't say it's been one of the highlights of my life.'

'You're not three,' said Michael unarguably.

'No.' Rosalind sighed and pushed her plate aside.

'Roz, look!' Jamie clutched at her in excitement and pointed out of the window. 'Lorry!'

'I know. It's exciting, isn't it?' She smiled at her little brother without thinking, and Michael felt his mouth dry. He remembered that smile so well. It had burned in his mind long after he had told himself that he had forgotten her.

He made himself look away. 'If Jamie's supposed to be our son, we'd better be ready to explain why he calls you Roz instead of Mummy,' he said, for something to say, anything to stop her smiling and let him start breathing again.

It worked. A slight crease appeared between Rosalind's brows as she turned back to him. 'I hadn't thought of that,' she said slowly. 'I don't know... Could we say that we're very progressive parents?' she suggested doubtfully.

'I don't think either of us looks the part,' said Michael dryly. 'Why don't we just say that he's adopted, and hope that Aunt Maud doesn't ask any more questions?'

'All right.' Rosalind rested her chin on her hands. 'Oh, dear, there's so much to think about, isn't there? I thought that once we left London I could stop thinking for a while, but I suppose we haven't really agreed on a proper story that we're going to tell people.'

'It shouldn't be too difficult,' said Michael. 'If anyone asks you what it's like living on a site, just tell them that it's hot and dusty. It's no use pretending that you know anything about archaeology, so you can say that you spend your time looking after Jamie. That should satisfy them—nobody's ever really interested when they ask those kind of questions anyway.'

'I suppose not,' said Rosalind doubtfully. 'What if anyone wants to know how we met or where we got married, that kind of thing?'

A hint of impatience crossed Michael's face. 'Tell them the truth—but not the whole truth, of course,' he said with a cool look. 'We can still have met through Emma. All you have to do is imagine what life would have been like if you'd married me five years ago.'

'Given that you weren't in love with me after all, absolutely disastrous, I expect!' she said tartly.

So that had rankled, had it? All the better, thought Michael. It wouldn't do Rosalind any harm at all to discover that she wasn't quite as irresistible as she thought she was. 'Quite,' he agreed, unmoved, 'but there's no need to tell anyone else that, is there? As far as anyone else is concerned, you're a friend of my sister, we met, fell in love and got married. I suggest, however, that if you don't want people to know who you are, you keep things simple. Don't start inventing any extravagant weddings or anything like that.'

'Don't worry, I haven't got a vivid enough imagination to picture you doing anything extravagant!' said Rosalind, stirring her coffee with a sour expression. 'If anyone asks, I'll tell them we had a very boring wedding and are now leading a very boring life together. They shouldn't have any trouble believing it when they see me wearing those frumpy clothes you made Emma buy for me!'

'You should be glad you've got such a convincing disguise,' Michael pointed out, and she glanced at Jamie, still happily absorbed watching the traffic, and sighed again.

'I know I should.'

'All this talk of weddings reminds me about another thing we didn't think about...' He dug in his pocket for the ring Emma had pressed into his hand that morning. 'Emma gave me this just before I left to pick you up this morning. Another thing you didn't think about. She said that from what she remembered of Aunt Maud, the first question she would ask would be why you didn't have a wedding ring.'

Rosalind put a hand to her mouth in dismay. 'Of course! I should have thought of that myself when I took off my engagement ring last night.'

'I'm glad you had the sense to leave that behind anyway,' said Michael crisply. 'It's much too ostentatious for a mere archaeologist's wife. Here, you'd better put it on and complete your disguise.'

He held out the ring to Rosalind, who took it and let it rest on her outstretched palm. 'Where did Emma get it from?' she asked.

'It belonged to our mother.' Michael saw her look down at the ring with a doubtful expression. 'Aren't you going to put it on?'

'I don't think I should,' she said slowly.

He frowned. 'Why not?'

'Because I know how much it means.' She touched the ring gently. It was a plain band of warm gold, slightly worn on one side. 'Emma's treasured this ring ever since your mother died.'

There was a short silence. 'I didn't realise you knew our mother,' said Michael after a moment. 'I thought she died before you met Emma.'

'She did, but that was part of the reason Emma and I have always been so close. We'd both lost our mothers when we were sent away to boarding school, and I suppose we gravitated together because of that. We helped each other through that first awful term, and the holidays when it seemed that everybody had a mother to go home to except us.'

Rosalind cradled her hands around her cup. 'Emma would talk about your mother all the time.' Lifting her eyes, she smiled a little wistfully at Michael. 'I used to wish my mother had been like yours...she sounded so lovely.'

'Yes, she was,' said Michael, remembering.

'My mother never did any of the things your mother would do,' Rosalind went on. 'She never read me a story or showed me how to bake a cake or kissed it better when I fell over and hurt myself. All I really remember about her is her perfume and the sound of her laugh.'

Michael looked down at his own coffee, wondering if he would have understood Rosalind better if he had known about her mother five years ago. They had never talked like this before, when she had seemed intent on proving to him how frivolous and superficial she was, but perhaps that had been his fault. Why should she have told him about her childhood if he hadn't asked?

'Didn't you see your mother after she left?' he asked.

'A couple of times, but it wasn't very successful. Things didn't work out for her in Hollywood. The film was a flop, and after that her parts got smaller and smaller.' Rosalind shrugged. 'My mother wasn't equipped to deal with failure. She opted out in the usual way. Every now and then she would check herself into a rehabilitation centre, but her recovery never lasted. Nothing ever lasted with my mother.' Rosalind's voice was laced with remembered bitterness. 'By the time I was twelve she was dead.'

'I'm sorry,' said Michael inadequately, and she flashed him a bright, meaningless smile.

'Don't be. I never knew her well enough to miss her. It was far, far worse for Emma. She cried herself to sleep every night.' Her fingers had closed over the wedding ring, but now she opened them again to look down at it. 'From what Emma told me, your mother was a very special person. She believed in things like love and marriage and her family.' Rosalind picked up the ring from her open palm and handed it back to Michael. 'It wouldn't feel right to wear her ring just as part of a pretence. I think it would cheapen it.'

Michael was silent as he turned the ring between his fingers. He had been seventeen when his mother died, and it had been hard, but not as hard as it had been for his little sister. He had promised to help look after Emma, and he had done his best to support her, although now it seemed that it had been Rosalind who had been there for her when it really counted.

'Emma wants you to wear it,' he said at last, and risked a look into Rosalind's eyes. They were warmer and greener and more direct than he had ever seen them before. His mother would have been appalled at the thought of a child growing up as Rosalind had done, with everything that money could buy except love and attention. 'I think my mother would have wanted you to wear it too,' he said slowly.

'Don't you mind?' asked Rosalind hesitantly, and he shook his head.

'No.' Michael didn't understand himself why it suddenly seemed important that she wear the ring, so he fell back on the most reasonable excuse he could find. 'What I *will* mind is if anyone thinks you're not really my wife,' he said. 'I don't want to look a fool in front of my aunt or any of her friends, and I don't want to hurt her either, by letting her even suspect that we're not what we're claiming to be. That would just be humiliating for all of us.'

To forestall any further argument, he held out an imperative hand. 'Give me your hand,' he ordered, and after only a tiny hesitation Rosalind placed her left hand on his open palm.

Michael looked down at the slender fingers laid on his and told himself not to think of how different things might have been if she had married him five years ago. Then this would have been a real ceremony, and the ring would have symbolised love and trust and commitment. All the things that Rosalind didn't believe in, in fact, he reminded himself brutally, and pushed the ring brusquely onto her third finger before he had a chance to change his mind.

'With this ring, I thee disguise,' he muttered, in an attempt to defuse the moment.

'Just for a month,' Rosalind added, sounding oddly breathless, and he nodded.

'Just for a month.'

They both looked down at their hands and Michael was taken aback to see that his fingers had closed around hers, as if of their own accord. He was about to drop her hand, and it would all have been all right if he hadn't made a big mistake and looked into Rosalind's eyes. They were soft and shimmering, drawing Michael down into their bewitching green depths as the rest of the world evaporated along with the air in his lungs.

They were cocooned together at their table in a bubble of silence. The traffic kept on swishing past the window, and people were moving busily around the restaurant, but they were all faded somehow and vaguely unreal.

Michael looked at Rosalind and was aware only of the warmth of her fingers curled around his, of the green of her eyes and the length of her lashes and the slow slam of his heart. He forgot how to breathe, forgot how to think, forgot everything except how much he wanted to kiss her again.

He was even tightening his grasp on her hand, to pull her across the table towards him, when a crow of delight from Jamie broke through the invisible sound barrier between them and rescued Michael from the brink of disaster.

'Look! Look, a digger! On a lorry!'

Rosalind and Michael snatched their hands back as if stung. A faint hint of colour tinged Rosalind's cheekbones as she devoted herself to Jamie, marvelling at the idea of a digger being transported on the back of a truck, and Michael was grateful for the fact that she was studiously avoiding his gaze. It gave him the chance to reinflate his lungs and pull himself together.

Appalled at how close he had come to making an idiot of himself all over again, Michael drank his coffee with savage concentration. What had he been thinking of, mooning into Rosalind's eyes like that? She would think he was the still the same besotted fool he had been five years ago! Michael's pride rebelled at the thought. Rosalind had taught him a hard lesson, and it wasn't one he should forget, no matter how beguiling her eyes!

Out of the corner of her eye, Rosalind saw him stare broodingly down into his cup, his face closed and hard. It was hard to believe that he was the same man who had held her pinioned by that piercingly light gaze while the touch of his fingers burned into her skin. Rosalind's heart was still looping around her chest, and she was making herself breathe very slowly and carefully in case she ran out of what little breath she had left. It had all whooshed out of her when Michael had slid the ring onto her finger, and now she couldn't seem to get it back.

Her finger throbbed beneath the ring. She wished she didn't have to wear it. It seemed too bitter a parody of what might have been. Rosalind's cheeks burned with humiliation when she thought about the way she had clutched at Michael's hand and stared stupidly into his eyes. What if he thought that she was regretting having turned him down? What if he even *guessed* that she had been sitting there imagining what it would be like if they *had* been married, and she could just lean over the table and kiss him?

Terrified that Michael had suddenly developed an ability to read her mind, Rosalind retreated behind a barrier of prickly hauteur and maintained what she hoped Michael would interpret as a bored silence for the rest of the journey. It didn't stop her being agonisingly conscious of Michael, who drove with a set expression. Oh, God, what if he was cringing at the idea of her clinging onto his hand, or working out how to tell her that she had had her chance and wasn't going to get another one?

Rosalind squirmed in her seat. *She* was supposed to be the one who was coolly detached from any messy emotion! She had decided a long time ago that it was better not to get too deeply involved with anyone, and experience had proved her right. Not that she was in any danger of getting involved with Michael again, Rosalind reassured herself hastily. It was just that whenever he moved his hands on the steering wheel, or turned his head slightly to check his mirror, her heart lurched and the breath stuck in her throat.

The constrained atmosphere was making her feel edgy

and unsettled. It grew tighter and tighter, and more and more difficult to break the silence, so that by the time they got to Askerby, Rosalind felt as if the slightest thing would make her snap.

Askerby itself turned out to be a quiet Yorkshire village built around a rough and irregularly shaped green. The big house on the outskirts had long been converted into a hotel, but the village was still prosperous enough to merit a church, two pubs and a small shop-cum-post office where Michael stopped to ask directions.

His great-aunt, it appeared, lived in an old house set back from the village green. It was built of warm brick, and from a distance the big Georgian windows and tangled garden gave it a picturesque air. On closer inspection, however, the path was overgrown and neglected and the paintwork peeling.

Rosalind eyed the house dubiously, leaning forward to peer past Michael as he pulled up outside the gate. 'It looks a bit grim, doesn't it? Perhaps we could suggest that we stay in that hotel we passed?' she suggested. 'Not so much work for your aunt?'

'She's not going to do any work,' snapped Michael, on whom the edgy atmosphere had obviously also had an effect. 'We're going to do it all for her—or, rather, you are.'

'Me?'

'Yes, *you*!' he said, getting out of the car. 'Judging by the state of the garden, Aunt Maud needs help, so you can take that exquisite nose of yours out of the air right now and think about looking after someone else for a change! There'll be no servants here to wait on you hand and foot, so if you want my aunt and anyone else you happen to meet to think that you're really married to me, you'd better be prepared to get your hands dirty.'

Rosalind slammed the door shut as she got out too. 'I don't know anything about cooking and cleaning!' she cried over the car roof.

'Then it's high time you learnt,' said Michael unsympathetically. 'It won't kill you. Having made such an almighty fuss to get here, I would have thought the least you could do in return for an old lady's hospitality was a bit of housework, but if you're not prepared to do it with good grace, you'd better say so now, before I make a fool of myself by introducing you to my aunt as my wife.

'It's up to you, Rosalind,' he went on, closing his own door. 'As far as I'm concerned, you can spend the rest of your life holed up in that hotel, but if you stay here, you earn your place. I don't care one way or another, but you'd better make up your mind now.'

Michael met Rosalind's smouldering green gaze across the car. 'Well?' he said. 'Do you want me to drive you back to the hotel?'

For an instant, she wavered. She hadn't planned on spending her time as an unpaid cleaning lady, and there was no doubt that a hotel would be more comfortable than this dilapidated-looking house. She wasn't sure she could cope with a month of Michael in the kind of mood he had been in for the last two hours, either.

The only trouble was, could she cope *without* him?

It was unsettling to think that Michael had been back in her life for barely more than twenty-four hours, and already she had come to rely on his cool, controlled presence. He might not be the easiest of companions, but she was safe with him, and so was Jamie. The thought of being thrown back on her own devices was unappealing. This, after all, was what she had wanted. It had cost Rosalind a lot of pride to ask Michael to take her with him, and it would be stupid to jeopardise her disguise now that she had got this far.

'No,' she admitted rather sullenly. 'I want to stay with you.'

CHAPTER FOUR

'IF YOU stay, you'll do whatever's needed.' Michael was obviously determined to rub her nose in it. 'If it means that you have to spend the next month scrubbing floors, that's what you'll do. Is that clear?'

'Perfectly,' said Rosalind through gritted teeth.

Opening the back door, she unclipped a restless and wriggling Jamie from his car seat and helped him out of the car. 'Any other conditions you'd like to lay down while you're at it?' she asked with dangerous sweetness as they made their way round the car to join Michael at the gate.

He surveyed her coolly. Her face was vivid with temper, the green eyes stormy and her mouth compressed into an irritated line.

'Now you come to mention it, yes, there is.'

'What is it this time? Chopping wood? Digging the garden every day? Or will working my fingers to the bone inside the house be enough for you?'

'A little acting should be sufficient,' said Michael, a muscle beginning to beat in his jaw. 'I don't want you to give Aunt Maud, or anyone else you happen to meet up here, any reason at all to suspect that you are not in fact my wife. That means behaving as if we're a normal loving, affectionate couple, and not as if you can't stand the sight of me, which is how you look at the moment. What's Aunt Maud going to think if you march up to the door in a flaming temper?'

'She'll probably think that I'm a loving, affectionate

wife who's just had a row with her incredibly irritating husband!' Rosalind snapped back.

She made to stalk past Michael through the gate, but he caught her arm and pulled her back round to face him. 'I'm serious, Rosalind!' he said tightly, clearly only hanging onto to his own temper with difficulty. 'I quite realise that loving isn't something that comes to you naturally, but I want your promise that you'll at least try to act as if it does.'

Rosalind wrenched her arm out of his grasp and made a show of rubbing it where his hard fingers had gripped her. 'I hope you're not expecting me to spend the next month hanging round your neck?'

'No.' Michael sucked in an exasperated breath. 'I just want us to act like a normal couple, so that anyone meeting us will assume that we're married because we love each other. Is that so hard?'

'That rather depends on your acting,' she said, shaking her hair back defiantly.

'We'll both need to do some acting,' said Michael, 'but as long as no one guesses that we *are* acting, I'm prepared to do my best.'

Rosalind eyed him with resentment. There was no need for him to make quite such a big deal out of how hard he would have to work to pretend to be in love with her!

'Well?' he went on inexorably. 'Are we agreed?'

'Oh, all *right*,' snapped Rosalind. 'I'll be the perfect, adoring little wifey, if that's what you want.'

'I do. Whether you will be able to look adoring convincingly unless you're looking in a mirror is another matter!'

'It'll be interesting to see how *you* get on without your

perfect little archaeologist friend to gaze at!' retorted Rosalind, provoked.

'I'm not expecting to find it easy,' said Michael tightly, 'but at least I know how a man and woman behave when they're in love, which is more than you do.'

'Oh, really?' Her voice dripped with sarcasm. 'If you're so clever at it, perhaps you'd better give me some tips?'

'Perhaps I should,' said Michael, and before Rosalind had realised what he was doing he had taken her by the waist and drawn her briskly towards him. 'God knows, you could do with the practice!'

Rosalind found herself hard against a compact, unyielding body, and her hands came up automatically to his chest, to ward him off. 'Wh-what are you doing?' she stammered, her blood pounding with alarm, confusion and a deep, insidious excitement that she did not dare admit even to herself.

'I'm taking your advice and showing you how it's done.' Almost casually, Michael slid one hand round her waist to pull her closer, while the other lifted to smooth her hair behind her ear. 'When loving couples have a row,' he explained, 'they kiss and make up rather than continue the argument in front of anyone else, as you were just about to do.'

'I...I'll bear it in mind,' said Rosalind unevenly as he feathered his thumb almost thoughtfully along her jaw to trace the outline of her mouth. Shaken by the discovery that it still took no more than a tantalising touch of his hand to set her drumming with anticipation, she tried to step back, but Michael's hold only tightened.

'I think you'll have to do better than that,' he said. For an airless moment he stood there, searching her face with his eyes, and then his mouth came down on hers and the ground seemed to drop away beneath Rosalind's feet.

Involuntarily, she clutched at his jumper, gasping at the sensation of falling, spinning, plummeting back through the years. His lips were firm and as electrifyingly warm as she remembered, and her own parted as if of their own volition, until, quite without knowing how it had happened, she was kissing him back, just as she had kissed him before, helpless before the terrible, tantalising, irresistible rush of pleasure.

It was as if the last five bleak years had never been. She melted into Michael, her arms sliding around him, pulling him close, heedless of everything but the intense, honeyed delight cascading through her veins, and murmured recognition deep in her throat.

And then, just as her hands were tugging feverishly at his jumper, impatient for the feel of the hard body below, it was over. Michael was lifting his head and putting her abruptly away from him. He drew a rather ragged breath. 'I think you're getting the idea,' he said.

His voice sounded hoarse, but otherwise he seemed unmoved, and Rosalind could only stare uncomprehendingly at him with dark, unfocused eyes. Disorientated, she shook her head to clear it, but it didn't seem to help. Her legs felt as if every bone had dissolved, and her skin was jumping and twitching as if she were in shock. She opened her mouth, but no words came out, and she had no idea what she had been going to say. What *was* there to say?

Kiss me again.

The answer jumped into her mind with such clarity that for one terrifying moment Rosalind thought that she had spoken them aloud. She swallowed. 'There...there was no need for that.'

'Oh, I don't know,' said Michael, regarding her with a considering air. 'It may have been more of a practical demonstration than you would have preferred, but the lesson seems to have worked. You don't look at all cross any more. In fact,' he went on, 'you really look quite convincing as a loving wife now.'

A wave of humiliation swept over Rosalind as she realised how her reaction must have seemed to him. Instead of laughing him off, or coolly brushing him aside as she would have been able to do with anyone else, she had wrapped herself around him and melted into his kiss with hardly even a token protest. For a girl determined to prove to him that she had absolutely no regrets about the past, she wasn't going about things the right way at all.

Rosalind longed to put Michael back in his place with a cutting remark, but she was afraid that nothing she could say would sound very convincing when only a minute ago she had been kissing him with what now seemed like a foolhardy lack of concern for the consequences.

Perhaps, after all, it would be more dignified to ignore the whole issue. Her eyes slid uncomfortably away from Michael's ironic grey ones, only to encounter a disapproving brown gaze. Jamie, bored of waiting for them to leave the gate, had come back to stare at her.

'What are you doing?' he demanded.

Rosalind moistened her lips. 'You'd better ask Michael that,' she said a little shakily, and Jamie turned obediently.

'What are you doing, Michael?'

'I was kissing Rosalind,' said Michael, without even the grace to sound embarrassed.

'Why?'

'We were just practising.'

'Why?'

'Why don't you go and ring the bell, Jamie?' Rosalind interrupted quickly as he opened his mouth to ask why again. Her voice felt croaky, as if it belonged to someone quite different, but she wasn't up to one of Jamie's endless interrogations right now. Her body was still zinging from Michael's kiss, and it was all she could do to stand upright by herself.

Nodding self-importantly, Jamie rushed up the overgrown path to stand on tiptoe and press the old brass bell by the front door. It was opened a few moments later by a straight-backed old lady with silver hair, beaky patrician features and an astringent manner.

'Mrs Brooke? Aunt Maud? I'm Michael.' He put an apparently casual arm around Rosalind's waist. 'This is my wife, Rosalind...and Jamie.'

Burningly conscious of his touch, Rosalind somehow managed a weak smile. 'Hello.'

Maud inspected them. Her eyes were dark, but they had the same unnervingly acute quality as her great-nephew's. Rosalind couldn't see any sign of the confused old lady that Michael had been so keen to protect in London. It felt as if Maud could see right through her, and was about to denounce her not only as a fraud but a bad actress, but in the end she only held the door open and stepped back.

'Come in,' she said. 'I'm glad to see you.'

She showed them into a dark, rather old-fashioned sitting room. The air was chill, as if the room wasn't used very often, but Rosalind's legs were still trembling with reaction from Michael's kiss and she was grateful for the chance to sit down.

Michael sat next to her, talking easily to Maud about

motorways and the country roads north of York, and she eyed him with obscure resentment. He might have assumed the burden of conversation, but he had no right to sound so normal, so unconcerned. *His* legs weren't wobbling, and if his heart was ricocheting around his chest like hers was, he wouldn't be able to sit there and talk about traffic and weather and what an attractive village Askerby seemed without even a *hint* of breathlessness.

Why did Michael have this odd effect on her? There was nothing special about him. He was sitting back in the sofa, apparently relaxed, dressed conventionally in a dark green jumper and biscuit-coloured chinos. He looked perfectly ordinary, Rosalind thought almost crossly. He had no business making her feel the way he did.

The initial pleasantries over, Maud produced some disgustingly weak coffee in exquisite porcelain cups, and seated herself stiffly in a chair by the unlit fire. 'I didn't realise you had a wife,' she said to Michael with a faint air of accusation. 'I suppose I should have expected it, though. You must be about thirty by now.'

'Thirty-one,' Michael agreed, apparently not in the least put out by his aunt's brusque way of talking.

'Have you been married long?'

'Five years,' he said, without looking at Rosalind.

'Hmm.' Maud's formidable gaze swept over to Rosalind, who had just managed to recover some of her poise. 'You must have been very young when you were married,' she commented with a disapproving look. 'You don't look very old now.'

'I was twenty-one,' Rosalind began coolly enough, and then was mortified to discover that her carefully collected composure crumbled the instant Michael ran a casual hand down her back.

'You were old enough to know what you wanted, weren't you, darling?' he said.

They were both looking at her. She had to say something. 'Yes,' was the best Rosalind could do, and even then it came out as barely more than a squeak.

Maud lifted her brows in faint surprise. 'Are you all right?'

'I'm fine.' Rosalind cleared her throat and tried again. 'I'm fine. Just a little tired, that's all.'

'You've had a long journey,' Maud conceded. 'I'm grateful to you both for coming all the way from the Middle East to see me, especially when it's such a long time since I've been in touch with your side of the family.' She turned to Michael with a trace of sadness. 'You can't have been much more than ten when I saw you last.'

'I was nine,' he said. 'Uncle John taught me how to play chess.'

'I remember.' Maud's strong face softened momentarily. 'You were all legs and ears. Oh, dear, what a long time ago it seems! If it hadn't been for that stupid argument with your grandmother, I could have seen you growing up. I might even have been to your wedding.' She sighed. 'Oh, well, I'm an old woman now and it's too late for regrets.'

'You said in your letter that you were anxious to sort out Uncle John's affairs,' Michael prompted, obviously deciding not to enlighten her about the wedding she hadn't missed after all.

'There's a whole roomful of papers I haven't touched since he died,' Maud told him. 'I want to move somewhere smaller and more convenient—I can't cope with this house any longer—but the truth is that I don't know where to begin. I'm not even sure how much money I have left, and all the documents are so complicated I can't make head or tail of them.'

'Well, we can certainly help you with that,' said Michael reassuringly. 'I'll go through all your papers so you know exactly where you stand, and Rosalind can help you sort out the house.' He smiled at his great-aunt and Rosalind was amazed that she couldn't hear the ironic undercurrent to his voice. 'Rosalind's been used to having servants while we've been overseas,' he explained, 'so it will be quite a change for her to do some cooking and cleaning for herself.'

Unfairly, he reached out and smoothed a strand of hair behind Rosalind's ear. 'She's quite looking forward to it. Aren't you, darling?'

Rosalind smiled through set teeth. 'I can't wait.'

'I remember what it's like.' Maud obviously hadn't heard her sarcasm either. 'My father was in the Colonial Office and I spent most of my married life overseas as well. The first time John and I came home on leave, I had never even baked a cake!'

'Really?' marvelled Rosalind, who never had either.

'It looks like you've found a kindred spirit,' observed Michael with a slightly malicious smile.

'Oh, I'm sure you're a lot more competent than I ever was,' said Maud. 'Girls nowadays have to be.'

Michael looked at Rosalind, at the long, beautifully manicured hands. 'That rather depends on the girl,' he said.

'And this is your room.' Maud opened the door into a bedroom cluttered with a handsome mahogany wardrobe, two chests of drawers and an old-fashioned dressing table.

Not to mention a small, old-fashioned double bed.

Rosalind looked at it in dismay. She had been deliberately putting off the moment when she would have to think about sharing a room with Michael but she couldn't avoid it any longer. As a bed, there was nothing wrong with it. For one person, it would be comfortable, for two lovers, cosy. But she and Michael weren't lovers any more, and for them it would be unbearable.

Every time she breathed out she would touch him, thought Rosalind in something close to panic. The very idea made her churn with nerves. How could she sleep next to him when the slightest movement would mean her skin brushing his, when rolling over would bring her slap up against his hard, unyielding body?

Why couldn't Maud have twin beds in her spare room like anybody else?

'Er...what a nice room,' she managed, avoiding Michael's glance.

'I can't remember the last time it was used,' Maud admitted with a disparaging look around. 'I hope you won't be too uncomfortable.'

'We'll be fine,' said Michael briskly.

He might be fine, but Rosalind was pretty sure she wouldn't be.

After some polite argument, it was agreed that Maud would take Jamie downstairs and make some tea while Michael went to get the cases from the car. Rosalind was left to start making the beds. She eyed the pile of sheets and blankets somewhat dubiously. Her experience of making beds was limited to shaking a duvet every now and then. Still, it couldn't be that complicated, could it?

When Michael walked back into the room with the cases, Rosalind had laid a sheet on the bed and was carefully unfolding it like a parcel. 'Don't tell me you've never made a bed before!' he sighed.

His sudden appearance made her heart bump against her ribs, but she did her best to ignore it. 'Of course I have,' she said, although not with much conviction. 'Just not like this.' She lifted the sheet to her face, wrinkling her nose as she sniffed. 'It smells as if it's been shut in a damp cupboard for at least fifty years!'

'It'll be fine,' said Michael impatiently. He dumped the cases by the wardrobe and came over to whisk the sheet from her hands. 'Here! We'll never get to bed at that rate.' Shaking the sheet out with a brisk flick of his wrists, he let it billow and then drape itself neatly over the mattress. 'You do that side,' he ordered as he bent to tuck it in.'

'Yes, sir!' muttered Rosalind. She watched the deft movements of his hands and then stooped, doing her best to copy him.

When they got to the head of the bed, Michael reached out and automatically smoothed the middle of the sheet. Rosalind stopped in mid-tuck. His hand looked very brown against the white sheet, and his fingers were long and strong and somehow competent.

They were hands that could fix an engine or piece together fragments of a thousand-year-old pot. Warm, firm, capable hands that had once smoothed over her body the way they were smoothing over the sheet where tonight they were going to have to lie and not think about touching each other.

Rosalind's insides snarled themselves into a knot so tight and sudden that she drew a sharp breath, and she bent her head to concentrate fiercely on folding in the corner.

'If you're worrying about sharing a bed with me, you needn't,' said Michael without looking up, and Rosalind, disconcerted by his ability to know exactly what she was thinking, pushed her hair behind her ear and glared resentfully across the bed.

'I wasn't!'

Michael finished off his corner with quick competence and straightened. 'I'm quite capable of lying next to you without jumping on you,' he said as if he hadn't heard her furious denial, adding ironically, 'I'm famous for my self-control.'

'I didn't see much sign of it when you kissed me at the gate,' snapped Rosalind, provoked.

Michael chucked a couple of pillowcases across the bed. 'I had enough self-control to stop,' he reminded her. 'If it had been up to you, we might still be there! Or are you going to deny that you kissed me back?'

Rosalind felt the treacherous colour sweep up her cheeks, but she lifted her chin and looked at Michael with challenge in her green eyes. 'I thought you wanted a convincing performance?' she said.

'I'd forgotten what a quick learner you are,' said Michael dryly.

'I just hope you're not planning on any further demonstrations like that!' she said, stuffing a pillow fiercely into its case.

'That, Rosalind, depends on how convincing a wife you continue to be!'

'What could be more convincing than being prepared to get into bed with you?' snapped Rosalind. 'And before you ask again, I'm not in the least bothered about it. I'd rather not, of course, but there's no point in making a fuss about something that can't be helped, and it's not as if either of us is likely to take advantage of the situation.'

'Oh, why's that?' asked Michael politely.

'I would have thought it was obvious,' she replied with a frosty look. 'You've said that you're happy in your relationship with Kathy, and I'm perfectly happy with Simon.'

She saw Michael's brows lift in unspoken amusement, and she glared across the bed at him. It was time she proved that she was just as cool as him about the prospect of sharing a bed. Cooler, in fact. After all, *she* was supposed to be the sophisticated one around here!

'Anyway,' she went on, hoping she sounded more casual than she felt, 'it's not as if we haven't done it before.'

Clearly she hadn't convinced Michael, who looked predictably unimpressed by her attempt at nonchalance. 'It was rather different then, though, wasn't it?' he said, already on his second pillow. 'We won't be making love this time.' He glanced over at Rosalind's flushed face. 'Unless you want to, of course.'

'No, thank you!' In spite of herself, Rosalind was unnerved, but determined not to show it. She shook back her hair haughtily. 'It was all a long time ago,' she said, with a lofty look. 'I've got no desire to repeat the experience and I can't imagine that you do either.'

'Oh, I don't know.' Michael pretended to consider, and Rosalind had a nasty feeling that he knew that she wasn't nearly as cool and sophisticated as she liked to make out. 'I seem to remember enjoying it at the time, don't you?'

On the other side of the bed Rosalind managed a careless shrug and settled the pillows one on top of the other, which gave her a good excuse not to meet his eyes. 'It was OK,' she said. 'But we were young and inexperienced. My tastes have changed since then.'

She was rewarded by a fractional tightening of Michael's jaw. 'So what do your tastes run to now?'

'That's none of your business,' said Rosalind, catching the other side of the top sheet that he threw across to her. 'But they don't include patronising archaeologists, so *you* don't need to worry about tonight either! I'm sure I'll be able to keep my hands off you!'

It might be easy to convince Michael that the prospect of climbing into bed beside him left her unmoved, but Rosalind had rather more difficulty persuading herself. In spite of an evening spent reminding herself of all the reasons why she wasn't the slightest bit bothered by the thought of the night to come, the butterflies zoomed around her stomach when they could put the moment off no longer and said goodnight to Maud on the landing.

She *wasn't* nervous. That fluttery feeling inside her was due to the sub-zero temperatures in the house, that was all. Michael was holding the bedroom door open with what Rosalind was sure was mock courtesy. Putting up her chin, she walked past him into the room. If he so much as suspected that she wasn't as cool as she had claimed, she would never hear the end of it!

The bed seemed to loom out at her. Rosalind swallowed and looked away, hoping that she seemed casually unconcerned, but the sharp click as Michael closed the door made her heart bump breathlessly against her ribs and her legs felt suddenly weak.

At least Michael didn't notice. 'God, it's freezing!' he said, sitting down on the bed and hauling his jumper over his head. 'Aunt Maud must have a constitution of iron,' he added, his voice rather muffled through the wool. 'She didn't even seem to notice the cold.'

His head appeared out of the jumper and Rosalind suddenly realised that she was staring at it, remembering how her hands had crept beneath it to feel the soft cotton of his checked shirt over the steely strength of his body when he had kissed her by the gate.

Abruptly she turned her back and flipped open the lid of her case. What on earth had possessed her to start thinking about that kiss *now*? 'She told me that she didn't believe in central heating,' she said as she began searching through her case, heartened to discover that her voice was almost steady.

'I don't think she believes in any modern technology,' said Michael.

'You can say that again! No heating, no television, no dishwasher...and did you *see* that phone in the hall?' Rosalind was beginning to feel better. With her back turned to Michael and the bed, and Maud's spartan house to grumble about, she could almost persuade herself that the humiliating nervousness in her stomach had vanished. 'It's like living in a museum!'

'Think yourself lucky that she's moved with the times enough to have electricity installed,' Michael said ironically, and Rosalind pushed back her hair.

'Remind me to feel grateful when I'm a bit warmer!' She gave an exaggerated shiver. 'I wonder what it's like up here in winter? It's supposed to be spring now!'

'Maybe in London, but it obviously hasn't got to Yorkshire yet. Maud was telling me that they had snow a couple of days ago.'

'Oh, great!' Rosalind's fingers closed over her nightdress and she tugged it out of the case. It was her favourite, a long, elegant cream satin robe with tiny straps.

She pulled it uneasily through her hands. It was a beautiful thing, but it had been designed with seduction in mind, and in the circumstances it was the last thing she wanted to be wearing tonight.

She had been too desperate to get Jamie away from London to think about things like packing last night. She had thrown all the sensible outfits Emma had bought for her into a case, grabbed a handful of lingerie and hoped for the best. Now she wished she had given it a little more thought. The one time she really needed something frumpy to wear, she was stuck with the last word in glamour!

Still, it was too late now. Perhaps wearing it would help her to feel more like herself? After all, she *was supposed to be* glamorous, Rosalind reassured herself—at least, everybody said so.

Turning, Rosalind found that Michael was in the middle of shrugging off his shirt, and any confidence in her own glamour and sophistication instantly deserted her. What on earth was the *matter* with her? One look at that broad, brown chest with the dark hairs arrowing down to his flat stomach and she felt as gauche and awkward as a schoolgirl.

Hastily averting her eyes, she dropped the nightdress back into her case and sidled over to the door. 'Er, I'll just go and check on Jamie,' she muttered, and fled.

Jamie was sleeping, but the room felt cold. Hearing Michael go along to the bathroom, Rosalind nipped back to take the eiderdown from the bed so that she could tuck him in warmly. She straightened, and stood looking down at her little brother for a while, hugging her arms together against the cold, and remembering how frightened she had been for him in London. It might not be very comfortable here, but at least Jamie was safe, and she would do whatever it took to keep him that way.

Even if it meant climbing into bed next to Michael.

CHAPTER FIVE

MICHAEL was still in the bathroom when Rosalind got back to their room. Seizing the opportunity to strip off her clothes and change into her nightdress, she then had to jump up and down on the spot to keep herself warm, and wished that she had waited, even if it *had* meant undressing in front of him.

By the time Michael reappeared, rubbing his face with the end of a towel draped round his neck, Rosalind's teeth were chattering so violently that she could hardly speak. She was relieved to see that he was planning to preserve the decencies by wearing boxer shorts and a grey tee-shirt. Maybe if she could pretend she hadn't noticed his long, straight, muscled legs it wouldn't be too awkward after all?

In the event, the bathroom was so icy that when she had finished Rosalind was too cold to feel any awkwardness, or indeed anything at all. Michael or no Michael, she couldn't wait to get into bed and get warm. Hopping from side to side in her bare feet, teeth going like manic castanets, she banged the bedroom door shut in haste, switched off the main light and practically ran across the room to leap into bed beside Michael.

'You said the idea of sharing a bed didn't bother you, but I didn't expect you to be that keen!' he said dryly as the mattress bounced on creaky springs.

'I'd be keen to jump anywhere that was warmer than your aunt's bathroom!' Rosalind replied with a shiver. Clicking off the bedside light, she huddled down under the bedclothes until only the tip of her head was visible. 'I'm absolutely frozen!'

'You're not the only one, so there's no need to take all the blanket.' Michael tugged back a share. 'What happened to the eiderdown?'

'I took it for Jamie. It was really cold in his room.'

'What? Not nice and cosy like ours?'

Rosalind ignored the sarcasm. 'I thought his need was greater,' she said, jaw beginning to ache with the effort of keeping her teeth together. 'Do you think your aunt's ever heard of electric blankets?'

'You wouldn't be that cold if you wore a sensible pair of pyjamas instead of that skimpy satin thing you've got on,' Michael pointed out.

'I hate pyjamas,' said Rosalind unreasonably. Turning onto her side, she rubbed her feet together to try to warm them, and to distract herself from the fact that she was actually in bed with Michael.

Not that it seemed to be working. She rubbed harder, only to find the sole of her foot brushing against Michael's leg. He gave an involuntary yelp.

'Your feet are like blocks of ice!'

'I wouldn't know—I can't feel them any more,' she said, not entirely truthfully. She had jerked her foot away the instant it had come into contact with the warm, firm muscle of his calf, but it felt as if every millimetre of his skin, every rough, masculine hair, had burnt an imprint onto her toes. She shuddered again, but this time it was not just from the cold.

'Why don't you put some socks on?' said Michael irritably. 'At least they'd keep your feet warm, and it might save *me* the risk of frostbite!'

'It's too cold to get out of bed and find them,' she objected.

With an exasperated sigh, Michael reached out to switch on his bedside light. Ignoring her protest at the rush of chill air, he flung back the bedclothes, swung his legs out of bed and strode over to his case.

Rosalind hugged the blankets up around her face and peered over to see what he was doing. She could see the tendons in the back of his thighs as he bent over his case. He wasn't overly tall, but he was as taut and lean as she remembered, and his body had thickened out in the last five years so that he seemed more solid, more powerful. Rosalind thought of her foot grazing his skin, and, in spite of herself, her toes tingled and curled.

Michael gave a grunt of satisfaction as he pulled out a pair of walking socks, and as he turned she ducked back under the bedclothes.

'Here, put these on,' he ordered, tossing the socks across to her.

'I'll look ridiculous,' Rosalind grumbled, but she hoisted herself up into a sitting position so that she could pull them on.

'Not nearly as ridiculous as you look wearing a satin nightdress when it's as cold as this,' Michael pointed out gruffly, getting back into bed. 'Anyway, it's not as if anyone's going to see you. There's only me, and you don't care what I think, do you?'

'No.'

'Then what does it matter?'

'I don't know….' Rosalind waggled her toes experimentally in the socks. 'I suppose I just don't like feeling stupid. It's a question of image.'

Michael snorted. 'Your image isn't going to keep you warm! Why waste your time worrying about it, anyway? Nobody cares about it except you.'

'Simon does,' she said, before she could help herself. Simon was marrying her for her image.

'Well, Simon isn't here, and if he was, I'm quite sure he'd do what any man in my position would do and tell you to put the socks on and shut up!'

'I can't imagine Simon somewhere like this,' confessed Rosalind as she wriggled back down under the covers. 'He likes everything to be perfect.'

Michael reached for the light and the room was plunged back into darkness. 'Including you?' he asked.

'Especially me,' said Rosalind a little sadly, thinking of the endless functions Simon took her to, where she had nothing to do but smile and look immaculate. 'He'd be absolutely appalled if he could see me now.'

'Because you're wearing socks with your satin nightdress, or because you're tucked up in bed with another man?' asked Michael acidly.

'I don't think he'd like anything about the situation,' she said, with as much dignity as she could muster when her teeth were clattering uncontrollably.

The bed creaked as Michael tried to settle himself more comfortably, and Rosalind clutched at the side of the mattress to stop herself rolling against him. 'So what would Simon do about the situation?' Michael's voice came dryly out of the darkness. 'Apart from throwing up his hands at your unorthodox nightgear, of course.'

Rosalind tried to imagine Simon giving up a month of his time to sort out the affairs of a relative he hadn't seen for years, but she couldn't get further than picturing him handing a dossier over to his secretary to sort out for him. 'I expect he'd take one look at the house and sweep everybody off to the nearest five-star hotel,' she said slowly. It was the sort of grand gesture Simon *would* make.

'I expect he could afford to,' said Michael with something of a snap. 'Unfortunately, I can't, and I doubt very much that Maud would allow herself to be swept anywhere, so I'm afraid you're just going to have to put up with things. I suggest you stop complaining and try and get some sleep instead.'

It was all very well to say, but how did you fall asleep when you were rigid with the effort of not shivering? There was no doubt that the socks were a comfort, and her feet were definitely warmer, but the rest of her only felt colder by comparison. Rosalind curled up in the foetal position, with her back to Michael, and tried to pull the blanket closer around her, but when she tugged it she encountered determined resistance from Michael, who was keeping a firm hold of the edge on the other side of the bed.

'You might let me have a bit more of the blanket,' she protested.

'You've already got most of it,' Michael countered. 'I'm making do with a piece about the size of a postage stamp as it is. I can only warm an inch of myself at a time!'

Rosalind shivered. 'The blanket's not big enough.'

'It would be fine if you weren't insisting on clinging right on the edge of the bed like that,' he pointed out. 'There's a whole lot of wasted blanket in the middle, where you should be lying.'

'I'm perfectly comfortable where I am, thank you,' said Rosalind, but her lofty retort was rather spoiled by a violent shudder, and Michael sucked in an impatient breath.

'Come here!' Rolling over, he hauled her unceremoniously against him. Rosalind found herself jammed up against his long, unyielding body, and the shock was so great that for a few seconds she could only gasp like a landed fish. 'I said I was comfortable where I was,' she managed to squeak at last.

'You might have been, but I certainly wasn't!' said Michael, wrapping his arms briskly around her and drawing her into his side until she lay with her face pressed into his shoulder and one arm flat across his chest. 'We might as well try body heat, as there obviously isn't enough of this blanket to keep us both warm.'

Rosalind lay rigid, hardly daring to breathe, bracing herself against the hard reassurance of the arms tightened so firmly around her. One of his hands held her upper arm, warm and strong and inexpressibly comforting against her bare flesh. The other rested on the curve of her hip, securing her against the hard length of his body.

Her heart was knocking against her ribs and her throat was tight and dry. It would be so easy to relax into him and let herself remember how good it felt to be held by him.

Easy, but very dangerous.

'I...I don't know if this is a good idea,' she said with difficulty, her voice muffled against his tee-shirt.

'I don't know if it is, either,' said Michael frankly, 'but I want some sleep, and I'm not going to get any with you shivering away like a whippet on an iceberg all night. Think of it as first aid. If it makes it any easier, I'm cold, too.'

'I suppose there's no point in us both suffering,' she admitted grudgingly.

'Precisely,' he said. 'And in case you were wondering, this isn't an elaborate ruse to get my hands on you again. It's been a long day, we're both tired and we're both cold, and, frankly, I've got other things on my mind than resurrecting a disastrous affair! You're quite safe from me, so just try and relax.'

Relax? How could she possibly relax when she was close enough to feel his heart beat? When every breath he took reminded her of how lean and hard his body was? When she knew that all she had to do was slip her hand beneath the tee-shirt and she would be able to touch warm, bare flesh, just as she had been able to in the past, to smooth her palm over his flat stomach, to let her fingers drift along his flank and feel the tautness of his muscles, the sleekness of his skin?

How could she relax when the very darkness was alive with memories of the last time they had lain in bed together, of long, languorous hours making love, of Michael's hands playing possessively over her body, Michael's lips scorching patterns of fire on her skin?

And now he was here, tantalisingly, impossibly near. What would he do if she eased herself over him and pressed her mouth against his throat? Would he smile? Would he whisper her name? Would he slide his hand up her thigh, rucking up the satin so that he could explore her with his fingers? The image was so vivid that Rosalind stiffened, aghast at the way her thoughts were leading.

Michael must have felt her tense. 'For God's sake, Rosalind!' he said in exasperation. 'It's like holding a block of wood! Can't you relax better than that?'

'I'm cold,' said Rosalind defensively.

He sighed, but tightened his hold, rubbing his hand up and down her bare arm. Rosalind was excruciatingly aware of his warm palm and the long, capable fingers. She remembered how they had rested on the steering wheel, the sureness with which he had changed gear, and something shivered down her spine and lodged unsettlingly at its base.

Silence settled warily around them, brittle at first but cautiously unwinding until it seemed almost natural that after five long years they should be lying together again in the darkness, with only the sound of their breathing and the beat of their hearts between them. Gradually, very gradually, Rosalind allowed her taut, tense muscles to relax.

'Warmer?' Michael's voice came quietly out of the darkness.

'Mmm. You?'

'Yes.'

He might be uncomfortable, thought Rosalind, wondering if she was imagining the note of strain in his voice. Perhaps he was getting pins and needles in his arm? She really ought to move back to her own side of the bed. It would be much more comfortable for both of them.

On the other hand, she *was* beginning to feel a bit warmer. If she shifted away, she would only get cold again, and, although it might be easier not to be touching him, Michael would still be close enough to be unnerving. She might as well be unnerved and warm.

And Michael *had* said that he was cold, too.

Succumbing to temptation, Rosalind snuggled closer into him. Tomorrow, she would buy an electric blanket, and there would be no reason to rest her head on Michael's shoulder or feel his chest rising and falling beneath her arm in a slow, steady, infinitely reassuring rhythm, but tonight...well, one night wasn't going to change anything, was it?

Sighing deeply, she let the tension that had been buzzing in her bones since that first horrible letter had arrived seep away and tiredness stole over her. She was warm, she was comfortable, and she was safe. For now that was enough.

Michael felt Rosalind relax into sleep and didn't know whether to be glad or sorry. There had been something masochistic in his impulse to pull her into his arms, he thought, grimacing into the darkness above her head. He might have told himself that he was just being practical, might even have acknowledged that it would be easier than having her so tantalisingly close and just imagining how it would feel to hold her again, but part of him had known perfectly well what torture it would be.

As if to underline the point, Rosalind murmured something sleepily and shifted against him, and Michael was suddenly, shockingly aware of her breasts pressing into his side, of her nakedness beneath the skimpy night-gown. His muscles clenched in involuntary response. The satin nightdress was cool and slippery beneath his hand; it would slither over her skin if he rucked it up to explore the warm, slender body beneath—

Michael's mind veered abruptly away from dangerous territory and he forced himself to concentrate on his breathing. In, out. In, out. Calm, steady, in control. *First aid,* he had told Rosalind. *You're quite safe from me. I've got other things on my mind than resurrecting a disastrous affair.*

He wished she hadn't believed him. He wished she had turned her back and clung resolutely to her side of the bed instead of lying so soft and so warm and so tantalisingly close. He could feel her breathing softly against him. After five long years, she was back in his arms. Michael wondered why he couldn't hate her the way he had tried to hate her for so long. He should be remembering the long, bitter nights he had spent waiting for the hurt to fade, waiting for the time when he would stop missing her, not thinking about her softness or the way the scent of her skin reminded him of a summer garden at dusk, of heady air and soft light and lingering enchantment.

Or how utterly right it felt to hold her again.

Pale spring sunshine filtering through the curtains woke Rosalind the next morning. For a while she lay, blinking at it, trying to work out where she was, and then, as memory hit her, she struggled up against the pillows and turned to the other side of the bed.

It was empty. Only the indentations on the pillow showed that Michael had ever been there at all. Slowly, Rosalind pulled the socks off her feet, frowning as she remembered how cold she had been the night before. That had been the only reason she had spent the night cuddling up to him.

Hadn't it?

A hint of colour stained her cheeks as she thought about how comfortably she had snuggled into Michael's side. His body was so strong, so solid, so secure. It had felt terrifyingly right to be lying there with her head on his shoulder, her arm across him. Uneasily she recalled her own drifting imagination, how vividly she had been able to picture stealing her hand beneath his tee-shirt, kissing her way along his jaw…

What if Michael had guessed what she was thinking about? What if he thought that was what she had wanted all along?

With an abrupt movement, Rosalind flung back the bedclothes and stood up. She had been tired, that was all. Tonight would be different. She would buy a warm nightdress and an electric blanket and a heavy duvet; whatever it took to reassure Michael that she had no intention of spending the next month sleeping in his arms as if that was the only place she wanted to be. She would be cool and unconcerned, and she would make sure he knew that she was certainly not expecting any intimacy between them just because of last night.

Michael, Jamie and Maud were in the kitchen when Rosalind made her way downstairs. After surveying the outfits bought by Emma without enthusiasm, she had resigned herself to a pair of brown leggings and a warm brushed cotton shirt over a thin polo-necked jumper. Probably exactly the kind of sensible, practical clothes that Kathy wore the whole time, she thought, feeling suddenly depressed.

Michael was sitting at the end of the table, fingers curled around a mug and head bent down towards Jamie, who was holding forth thickly and largely incomprehensibly through mouthfuls of toast. Maud sat opposite, watching Jamie with an indulgent expression.

None of them had noticed Rosalind. Prepared to sail in and impress Michael with her complete lack of embarrassment, she found herself instead stopping dead at the sight of him, her heart missing a beat as if she had tripped on a stair.

Why did it *do* that? He was just an ordinary man, dressed in an ordinary green jumper, drinking tea from a perfectly ordinary mug. Unnoticed by the door, Rosalind studied Michael as if she had never seen him before.

His skin was brown from the years he had spent in the desert sun, and there were creases at the edges of his eyes. Rosalind could imagine him out in the middle of nowhere, squinting at an empty horizon, at home in the space and the light and the silence. He had brown brows and brown hair, still damp from a shower, and a straight, uncompromising nose. Rosalind's eyes travelled slowly over the lean planes of his face, down the line of his cheek and along the capable jaw to rest at last on the cool, quiet mouth, and the breath snared in her throat as she found herself remembering how it had felt when he kissed her.

As if sensing her sudden intake of breath, Michael looked up, his eyes startlingly clear and alert in his brown face, and Rosalind felt her stomach disappear in a dizzying rush, leaving her with a strange hollow sensation.

Maud looked round at the same time. 'Ah, there you are at last,' she said disapprovingly.

At last? Rosalind looked at her watch, glad of the excuse to look away from Michael's disconcerting gaze, and saw that it was only quarter to eight.

'Jamie and I thought you could do with a lie-in, didn't we, Jamie?' said Michael quickly.

'A *lie*—? Oh!' Belatedly Rosalind twigged that her own idea of a lie-in probably differed from Maud's by a good few hours. 'Oh, yes...thank you,' she said a little uncertainly, unaware of how different she looked that morning, with her face bare and her newly brown hair pushed behind her ears.

'Come and sit down.' Michael pushed back his chair abruptly. 'I'll make you some fresh tea—or would you prefer coffee?'

'Tea will be fine,' said Rosalind, remembering the disgusting coffee that Maud had produced the day before. Drawing a deep breath, she made her way over to Jamie and pulled out a chair beside him. She hoped it was just hunger that was making her feel so odd. She ruffled

Jamie's hair. 'Hello, you. What have you been eating?' she added, eyeing his jam-smeared face with mock disfavour.

'Toast,' Jamie told her. 'Aunt Maud doesn't have any coco pops.'

'She won't have any jam left either by the look of you!' Rosalind got up to find a damp cloth and wiped his face and hands, ignoring his muffled protests as she dealt with the sticky mess. It was funny how quickly you got used to doing jobs that had seemed revolting at first. Pushing back the hair which swung forward over her cheek as she bent over him, she smiled at Jamie.

As Rosalind straightened, she found herself looking straight into Michael's light eyes over the top of Jamie's head. They held such a peculiar expression that she stopped, the sticky cloth forgotten in her hand and the smile evaporating from her face. For a tiny, timeless moment, they stared wordlessly at each other, then Michael turned away and dropped the lid of the teapot into place.

'Tea,' he said. Careful not to touch her, he put the pot on the table, and poured her a mug as she sat down.

Rosalind found her eyes riveted on his fingers as they curled around the handle of the teapot, and with sudden, disturbing clarity, she pictured them as they had been last night, sliding warmingly up and down her arm, their imprint burning through the satin as they rested against her hip.

She swallowed. 'What's happening today?' she asked with forced vivacity.

'I've suggested to Aunt Maud that we go and do some shopping for her this morning.' Michael sat down as far away from her as possible. 'If that's OK with you?'

'Fine.' Thrown by his matter-of-fact manner, Rosalind

cupped her hands around the welcome warmth of her mug and stared down at the steam swirling gently up from the tea. Had she imagined that odd look in his eyes?

'We made a list,' said Jamie excitedly. He knelt up on his chair to lean on the table. 'I wrote it. Look!'

The piece of paper he held out was as liberally smeared with jam as his face had been. Rosalind took it gingerly by the edge and studied it. The list appeared to consist of a number of wavering Js and assorted scribbles. 'This will be very handy,' she assured him gravely. 'We'd better remember to take it with us.'

'Michael did one too,' Jamie admitted generously, pleased with her response.

'I must say you seem to have your husband very well trained,' Maud commented acidly. 'Insisting on lie-ins, making you tea, organising the shopping for you! I hope you know how lucky you are!'

That mixture of disapproval and sarcasm must be a Brooke family characteristic, thought Rosalind with an inward sigh, but, mindful of her promise to act the part of a loving wife, she forced a smile. 'I do,' she said.

'Yes, you look like a young woman who knows which side her bread is buttered,' Maud sniffed. 'The point is, what do you do for Michael in return?'

Rosalind's smile became rather fixed, and there was a spark of anger in her eyes as she lifted her chin and looked squarely back at Maud. 'I think that's between Michael and me!' she said.

To her surprise, Maud responded with a crack of laughter. 'There's no need to take that hoity-toity tone with me!' she said, her naturally acerbic tone laced with amusement. 'I've seen the way you look at each other.'

'Oh?' Had Maud seen her watching Michael from the

doorway? The colour rose in Rosalind's cheeks and she buried her face hastily in her mug. She wished Maud didn't have such uncomfortably shrewd eyes. Why couldn't she be a sweet, dotty old lady, unaware of much beyond her knitting?

'Oh?' said Michael at the same time, sounding for once rather nonplussed.

Maud lifted her brows. 'Why are you looking at me like that? You don't need me to tell you how you feel about each other!'

'No.' Michael's smile didn't quite reach his eyes. Reaching behind Jamie, he slipped his hand beneath Rosalind's hair and let it rest at the nape of her neck, while his thumb caressed the side of her throat. 'Rosalind knows exactly how I feel about her. Don't you, Rosalind?'

Clenching her spine to resist the shudder of pleasure caused by the light, tantalising brush of his thumb, excruciatingly aware of his palm against her nape, Rosalind turned her head very slowly to look at him. His hand was warm, his voice was warm, but his eyes were clear and cool and guarded. They were the eyes of a man who had been hurt once and wasn't going to be hurt again. He might have kept her warm last night, they warned, but that didn't mean he liked her any more than he had done the day he had walked out of her life five years ago.

'Yes,' she said bleakly. 'I do.'

'Do you know where you're going?' Rosalind broke the constrained silence as they drove down the hill and out of Askerby on a narrow country road. She had been obscurely hurt by the dislike in Michael's eyes, and was desperately trying to think of a way to impress on him that, as far as she was concerned, last night had been a one-off. She had no more desire to repeat the experience than he had, she told herself, closing her mind to the memory of warmth and comfort and indefinable reassurance.

'According to Aunt Maud, there's a superstore on the outskirts of York,' said Michael, his voice even cooler than her own. 'I thought it would be a good idea if we stocked up on a few essentials. There doesn't seem to be much in the house.' He took one hand off the steering wheel and fished in his jacket pocket for the list he had jotted down earlier, with Jamie's well-meaning but not very useful assistance. 'Have a look at this,' he said, passing it across to Rosalind, 'and see if there's anything else you want to add.'

Rosalind heard the coolness and was stung. She was damned if she was going to try and make him like her just because her insides tangled themselves into a knot whenever he looked at her.

There had been odd moments when she had wondered whether he might not dislike her quite as much as he had said, times when they had looked at each other and she could have sworn that the old chemistry still simmered between them, but his eyes over Jamie's head that morning had held a message that was as clear as a slap in the face. As far as Michael was concerned, she was still the idle, pampered girl who had rejected him so carelessly, and he wasn't about to change his mind, no matter how convincingly he might behave in front of his aunt.

She sighed as she glanced down the shopping list. 'I don't know… I don't usually have to worry about this kind of stuff when I go shopping.'

'Well, you'd better start worrying,' said Michael

flatly. 'There are no staff to do your shopping for you now! If you forget anything you need, you're just going to have to do without. The village shop has milk and bread and a few tins, but that's about it, and I'm not driving you into York every day, so if you've got any sense you'll start thinking for yourself right now!'

The novelty of being pushed around in a trolley kept Jamie amused, but Rosalind was less impressed by her first experience of supermarket shopping. The television commercials never showed the people who crashed their trolleys into yours, or stopped to chat right in middle of the aisle so that everyone had to manoeuvre awkwardly around them, or the impenetrable logic of the way the shelves were stacked.

Rosalind was thoroughly bored and cross by the time they had got through the check-out and loaded everything into the boot. 'Don't tell me we've forgotten something?' she sighed as she saw Michael relock the car and head back towards the shops. 'I don't think I could stand to go through all that again!'

Michael rolled his eyes. 'Only you could make a supermarket sound like a test of endurance! You don't need to panic, anyway. We're not going back.' He nodded his head across the car park. 'I saw an electrical store over there. With any luck, we'll be able to find a couple of heaters and an electric blanket.'

Obviously he wanted her firmly on her own side of her bed tonight. Well, that was what she wanted, too. Rosalind just wished she'd made the point first. 'Good idea,' she said in a brittle voice. 'We don't want to have to go through another night like last night, do we?'

Michael's expression was inscrutable. 'No,' he agreed, 'we don't.'

CHAPTER SIX

IT WAS starting to rain. The perfect end to a perfect day, Rosalind thought glumly as she turned up her collar. 'Come on, Jamie, let's go back,' she called.

The morning sunshine had long disappeared behind lowering black clouds, but she had been desperate to get out after a tetchy drive home from that awful supermarket and lunch spent being frigidly polite to each other in front of Maud. Afterwards, Michael and Maud had disappeared into the study to start going through the papers, Jamie had had a nap, and Rosalind had been left to clear up the kitchen yet again.

Fed up, she'd buttoned Jamie up in a blue duffel coat and red boots and dragged him out for a walk. Her childcare book said that he needed a stimulating routine, not that Rosalind had found the walk very stimulating so far. Nor had her temper improved. A cold wind was blowing her hair around, she had forgotten her gloves, and her shoes were ruined as she slithered along the muddy path.

And now it was raining. Thunder rumbled ominously and Rosalind looked up to see that the sky had turned black and that the drizzle was about to turn into an almighty downpour. She only just had time to get Jamie's hood up before the heavens opened. Her own jacket didn't even have a hood, so it looked as if she was going to have to get wet.

'Come on!' she shouted above the noise of the rain as she took Jamie's hand. 'We'd better run!'

They had walked further than she had thought, and both were drenched by the time they burst breathlessly into the kitchen. 'Ugh!' Rosalind banged the back door shut, and as she collapsed back against it turned to find herself being regarded by two pairs of eyes, one all too familiar and the other belonging to a complete stranger. Michael was sitting at the kitchen table with an elegantly-dressed blonde, and they were looking at her with surprise and not a little amusement.

Rosalind was suddenly very conscious of how she must look, bedraggled, mud-splattered and red-faced, gasping for breath as she leant back against the door. The water was streaming off the jacket which she had borrowed from Maud, and was puddling at her feet. There was rain running uncomfortably down her neck, too, from the hair which was plastered to her head.

There was a moment of silence, and then Michael pushed back his chair and came over to strip off Jamie's duffel coat and help him with his boots. 'Where on earth have you been?' he asked.

'For a walk,' said Rosalind, wearily wiping the rain from her cheeks.

'But it's pouring out there!'

'*Is* it?' She pretended to reel back in astonishment, and Michael's mouth turned down at the corners.

'You're both sodden,' he said. 'You'd better go and get those wet things off and then you can come and meet Laura.' He hung up the duffel coat and turned back to the table, with his hand on Jamie's head. 'As you've probably gathered, Laura, this here is Jamie, and—'

'And I'm Rosalind,' said Rosalind, with a dangerously bright smile. 'Michael's wife,' she added deliberately, just to make sure his new friend knew where she stood.

The blonde smiled. 'I'm Laura Osborne. Michael's been telling me about you.'

'Have you, darling?' simpered Rosalind, laying stress on the 'darling'. He had looked a little too cosy sitting next to Laura, and she wanted to annoy. She hung Maud's jacket next to Jamie's and laid a possessive hand on his arm. 'Not everything, I hope?'

'Of course not.' Michael didn't quite shake off her hand, but he moved back to the table. 'Laura lives in the village,' he told her. 'She's been very kind to Maud.'

Laura blushed and disclaimed. 'Honestly, I've hardly done anything. I enjoy her company.'

'That's not how Maud tells it,' he said warmly. 'She's told me how much you've done for her, and I'm very grateful. It was Laura's idea that Maud get back in touch with me,' he added in a noticeably cooler tone to Rosalind, who was easing off her ruined shoes.

'Really?' she said in a clipped voice. Michael was gushing over Laura enough for both of them, and she didn't see any need for her to join in too. It was some comfort to notice that in spite of her skilful make-up Laura was clearly older than she was. But there was no denying that she was attractive, with very blue eyes and soft blonde hair.

'She used to talk a lot about you and your sister, and how she regretted losing contact with you,' Laura was explaining to Michael, who had sat down beside her again and was watching her admiringly, clearly besotted. 'I think she just needed a push to write that letter, and I'm just glad it's worked out so well.' Rosalind's eyes narrowed as she saw the suspiciously intimate smile Laura exchanged with Michael. 'Maud's not very demonstrative, but I know that she thinks you're wonderful.'

YOU COULD WIN THE

£600,000.00
GRAND PRIZE

IN THE

BIG PRIZE DRAW

6 GAME TICKETS INSIDE!

ENTER TODAY!

Here are your BIG WIN Game Tickets potentially worth from £6.00 to £600,000.00 each. Scratch off the GOLD STRIP on each of your Prize Draw tickets to see what you could win and post your entry right away.

This could be your lucky day - Good Luck!

FOLD AND DETACH ALONG THIS LINE - RETURN ALL GAME TICKETS INTACT.

TICKET 1

Scratch GOLD STRIP to reveal potential value of cash prize and return to find out if this is a winning ticket.
Return all game tickets intact.

LUCKY NUMBER

0J 157905

THE BIG WIN

TICKET 2

Scratch GOLD STRIP to reveal potential value of cash prize and return to find out if this is a winning ticket.
Return all game tickets intact.

LUCKY NUMBER

GL 767214

TICKET 3

Scratch GOLD STRIP to reveal potential value of cash prize and return to find out if this is a winning ticket.
Return all game tickets intact.

LUCKY NUMBER

ZH 613309

TICKET 4

Scratch GOLD STRIP to reveal potential value of cash prize and return to find out if this is a winning ticket.
Return all game tickets intact.

LUCKY NUMBER

FP 273900

TICKET 5

Scratch GOLD STRIP to reveal number of books you will receive. These books, part of a sampling project to introduce romance readers to the benefits of the Reader Service, are FREE

AUTHORISATION CODE

193279-411

TICKET 6

All gifts are free.
No purchase required.
Scratch GOLD STRIP to reveal free gift, our thanks to readers for trying our books.

AUTHORISATION CODE

130107-742

YES! Enter my Lucky Numbers in the £600,000.00 Grand Prize Draw and when winners are selected, tell me if I've won any prize. If the GOLD STRIP is scratched off Ticket 5, I will also receive FREE Mills & Boon Enchanted® novels along with the FREE GIFT on Ticket 6. *I am over 18 years of age.*

N9GI

MS/MRS/MISS/MR ______________________
BLOCK CAPITALS PLEASE

ADDRESS ______________________

____

______________________ POSTCODE ______________________

Offer valid in the U.K. only and is not available to current Reader Service subscribers to the Enchanted™ series. Overseas and Eire please write for details. We reserve the right to refuse an application and applicants must be aged 18 years or over. Only one application per household. Offer expires 31st Jan 2000. Terms and prices are subject to change without notice. As a result of this application you may receive further offers from Harlequin Mills & Boon and other carefully selected companies. If you do not wish to share in this opportunity, please write to the Data Manager at the address overleaf.

THE READER SERVICE™: HERE'S HOW IT WORKS

Accepting the free books and gift places you under no obligation to buy anything. You may keep the books and gift and return the despatch note marked "cancel". If we don't hear from you, about a month later we'll send you six brand new novels and invoice you for just £2.40* each. That's the complete price – there is no extra charge for postage and packing. You may cancel at any time, otherwise we'll send you six more books, which you may either purchase or return – the choice is yours.

*Terms and prices subject to change without notice

Hand print your name and address on a postcard and send to: "BIG WIN", Harlequin Mills & Boon Ltd, PO Box 236, Croydon, Surrey, CR9 3RU.

The Reader Service™
FREEPOST CN81
CROYDON
CR9 3WZ

NO STAMP NEEDED

'Well, she thinks that about you, too.'

Rosalind is hackles rose. She hadn't realised Michael could look quite that fatuous! They could only have known each other an hour, and already they were all over each other! She tossed her ruined shoes aside, but before she had a chance to bring their revolting love-in to an end, Laura was off again. This time it was Rosalind's turn to be the object of her charm offensive.

'Maud's thrilled to see you and Jamie, too, of course. It was so lucky you could come with Michael.'

'Oh, we go wherever Michael goes,' said Rosalind, who had been quick to notice the absence of a wedding ring on Laura's hand. On her mettle, she went up behind Michael's chair and bent to put her arms over his shoulders, linking her hands on his chest and resting her cold cheek against his temple.

'We can't bear to be separated, can we, darling?' she added winsomely, smiling as she felt Michael stiffen, and then kissed his ear for good measure to ram the point home to Laura that he wasn't the unattached nephew she might have fantasised about, but had a real, live wife, who might look a bedraggled mess in comparison to her casual elegance, but who was more than capable of keeping too-friendly neighbours at bay!

Michael looked wooden. 'Don't you think you and Jamie had better go and get dry?' he said.

Rosalind was furious. Was that all he could say? So much for *his* acting! He could hardly have made it clearer that he wanted her out of the way so that he and Laura Osborne could carry on telling each other how wonderful they were!

Withdrawing her arms abruptly, she scowled and straightened, feeling as if she had been dismissed. She had little choice, though, but to take Jamie upstairs. No doubt Michael was already telling Laura how his wife didn't understand him, Rosalind thought sourly as she tugged off Jamie's trousers and found him a dry pair. Well, she had no intention of gratifying them by taking a bath or spending ages changing her clothes.

Peeling off her wet leggings as she went, Rosalind hopped into the bedroom and scrabbled through her case in search of something to wear that would put Laura bloody Osborne in her place, but Emma had interpreted Michael's brief to buy dowdy clothes a little too efficiently. The smartest thing Rosalind could find to wear was the hated brown corduroy skirt with a white shirt, but it was so cold that she had to ruin even that limited effect by shrugging on a particularly dreary cardigan as well. She looked in the mirror as she dragged a comb through her hair and sighed. There was no way she was going to impress Laura looking like that! Still, it was the best she could do. Rosalind hurried downstairs to break up their cosy tête à tête, but by the time she got there Laura was on the point of leaving anyway. She and Michael were saying goodbye at the door, and her understated grey outfit managed to make Rosalind feel even frumpier in comparison.

'I'm so sorry I've got to rush off,' said Laura as Rosalind descended the last steps, looking decidedly put out. 'I must go and pick up Tom from his childminder.'

'Laura's got a little boy the same age as Jamie,' Michael explained.

'A little boy?' Rosalind was momentarily taken aback. 'You're married, then?'

'Divorced,' said Laura pleasantly. 'Tom's four, so he is a little bit older than Jamie, but I'm sure they'd enjoy playing together. Why don't you bring him round tomorrow?'

'That sounds great,' said Michael quickly, before Rosalind had a chance to open her mouth. 'Jamie would like that. Wouldn't he, Rosalind?'

Rosalind managed to stretch her lips into a semblance of a smile. 'He'd love it,' she said, with little choice but to agree.

'Good, that's settled, then.' Laura drew on her gloves and smiled at Rosalind. 'I'm sorry I haven't had a chance to get to know you properly, Rosalind, but perhaps we can have a chat tomorrow? And if you're in York, you must come to my shop.'

'Laura sells clothes,' Michael said, as if Rosalind was supposed to be impressed.

'Oh?' she said coolly.

'I don't keep a lot of stock, just a few designer lines, but there are a few things in at the moment that you would look wonderful in.' She surveyed Rosalind with a professional eye. 'You know, you've got a great figure, and with that bone structure you could look absolutely stunning.'

Rosalind, who sat in the front row of all the big fashion shows, was speechless for once, and Michael, clearly spotting an opportunity to repay her for her saccharine performance in the kitchen, put his arm around her waist and gave her a squeeze. 'You should go, darling,' he said with a malicious smile. 'Laura would be a great person to give you some tips. You know you're always saying how you wish you could make more of yourself.'

The green eyes looked daggers back at him. 'But, *darling,*' Rosalind replied in a voice dripping with bitter honey, '*you're* always saying that you love me just as I am and you don't want me to change!'

'I know,' said Michael, patently enjoying himself. 'But I think Laura's right. Perhaps you do need to update your image a bit. All you need is a bit of expert advice and you could learn to look as nice as she does!'

'Thank you *very* much!' Rosalind wrenched herself out of Michael's arm and rounded on him the moment the door closed after Laura. *'Laura would be a great person to give you some tips,'* she mimicked him. 'That'll be the day!'

'It serves you right,' said Michael, unmoved. 'You're always so pleased with yourself about your clothes. I didn't think it would do you any harm to be on the receiving end of some advice for a change. You could certainly do with some,' he added, with such a disparaging look that Rosalind was stung.

'I happen to be famous for my sense of fashion,' she snapped.

'Maybe you are, but for my money Laura Osborne dresses a lot better than you do.'

'Anyone could dress better than I do at the moment, with those hideous clothes you made Emma buy for me.'

'I'm not talking about now,' said Michael. 'I'm talking about the way you usually dress. Laura was wearing effortless, stylish clothes that were appropriate for where she was and what she was doing.'

Rosalind curled her lip. 'That grey thing isn't what *I* would choose to try and seduce my neighbour's nephew,' she put in, but her sarcasm had no effect on Michael.

'No, you would try too hard,' he said in a voice tipped with steel. 'That's what I mean. Laura was understated and comfortable in a way that showed she was at ease with herself. You, on the other hand, dress for attention. All those flash clothes are designed to make sure that people look at what you're wearing and not at the person you really are inside.'

'Oh, so now you're a psychologist,' sneered Rosalind, more ruffled than she wanted to admit by his observation.

Michael shrugged, infuriatingly unmoved. 'I'm just saying that you could do worse than copy Laura's style if you want to look really well dressed.'

'When I want fashion advice I'll ask for it,' she hissed as she turned to stalk back upstairs. 'And it won't be from you or some patronising divorcee with a crummy clothes shop in York!'

'I don't know why you're being so unpleasant,' he said, following her up the stairs. 'I thought she was a very nice woman.'

'You made that pretty obvious!' snapped Rosalind. 'I'm *so* sorry I broke up your cosy little session. Anyone would think you'd known each other for ever!'

'Laura's an easy person to be with,' said Michael.

'Unlike me, I suppose?'

He rolled his eyes. 'No one could ever call you *easy,* Rosalind!'

'At least I don't pour out my life story within minutes of meeting someone for the first time!'

'Nor did Laura.'

Reaching the landing, Rosalind put her head round Jamie's bedroom door to see that he was playing quietly. 'You seem to have found out everything there is to know about her anyway! Laura's got a little boy, Laura's got a shop, Laura's good with old ladies…'

'Maud told me about her last night when you were putting Jamie to bed.'

'And where *was* Maud while all this mutual admiration between you and Laura was going on?' said Rosalind, banging into their bedroom.

'She went to have a rest just before you came back.'

'Very convenient!'

'Oh, don't be so bloody ridiculous!' snapped Michael. 'Anyone would think you were jealous.'

'*Jealous?* Hah!' She swung round, green eyes blazing. 'Do you honestly think I'm likely to be jealous about *you*?'

'No,' he said tightly, 'but you sound it.'

Momentarily taken aback by the realisation that she probably did, Rosalind recovered almost immediately to fight back. 'I'm not jealous. I'm angry. You made me look ridiculous in front of her,' she accused him.

'You did that all by yourself,' retorted Michael. 'What was all that simpering and carrying on in aid of?'

Rosalind was furiously gathering up the wet clothes she had left scattered on the floor in her haste to get downstairs and prise Michael and Laura apart. 'I thought you wanted me to behave like an adoring wife?'

'And was that revoltingly twee performance the best you could do?' Michael folded his arms and regarded her sardonically. 'God help Simon!'

'If we're going to talk about revolting, what about you and Laura?' she demanded, dumping the damp clothes onto a pile of washing. *'Oh, Laura, you're so wonderful,'* she mocked. *'No, Michael, you're more wonderful than I am*...it was absolutely disgusting! And, while we're on the subject, I was a lot more convincing as a wife than you were as a husband! You practically had a fit when I put my arms round you and pretended to show a little physical affection.' Rosalind shook her hair angrily away from her face. 'I don't know why you didn't just get out a barge pole to push me away and be done with it!'

Michael pinched the bridge of his nose in exasperation. 'I hope you're going to be a little more rational next time you see Laura.'

'What next time?' Rosalind was hunting through her bag for her mobile phone. 'You don't think I'm going over to her house to be patronised about my dowdy clothes again, do you?'

'It was stupid of me, I know, but I did think you might consider Jamie,' said Michael. 'If you read your book on childcare carefully I'm sure you'll discover what anyone else with any common sense knows, which is that children like and need the company of other children. Anyway, you're going to have to meet Laura again. Maud's asked her and a few other neighbours round for a drink next Friday.'

'Oh, great,' said Rosalind sourly as she tested the battery. 'That'll give Laura a chance to show off her evening collection!'

Michael sighed. 'It'll give *you* a chance to show off a few social skills. None of which have been in evidence so far,' he pointed out with an acid look.

'I don't need any lessons from you on how to behave at a party,' snapped Rosalind. 'Or on anything else,' she added, remembering how he had kissed her at the front gate. 'And now, if you don't mind, I'd like some privacy. I want to ring my fiancé.'

She waved her mobile at him, and Michael seemed to realise for the first time what she was holding. 'I thought you were going to leave your phone in London?'

'I changed my mind,' she said loftily. 'All my incoming calls are going to an answering service, but I wanted to be able to call Simon in private. Any objections?'

'None at all,' said Michael, heading for the door. 'I'm sure you need some reassurance after the terrible shock of finding someone better dressed than you are!'

Rosalind felt like throwing the phone at him, but he had gone. With an infuriated sound, she sat down abruptly on the bed. Simon hated being distracted by personal phone calls during the day unless it was urgent, and she had only said that she wanted to call him to annoy Michael, but perhaps, now she thought about it, she *did* need some reassurance. After all, her dress sense and her social skills were the very things Simon valued.

And right now Rosalind wanted to feel that somebody valued her for *something*. On an impulse, she dialled his number.

It was a mistake. Simon was preoccupied, obviously in the middle of a meeting. 'Oh, it's you, Rosalind,' he said, and she could hear him telling someone in the background that he wouldn't be long. 'What is it?'

No: How are you? No: Are you safe? No: I've been thinking of you. Just: 'What is it?'

Rosalind's fingers tightened around the phone. Well, that had been the deal, hadn't it? 'It's nothing,' she said. 'I just thought I'd ring and let you know that we arrived safely.'

'Nobody's recognised you?' Simon asked sharply.

'No.'

'Well, please don't do anything stupid. I can't afford a scandal. The party's taking a tough line on family values at the moment, and if the papers get wind of you running around the country with another man, they'll have a field day.'

From where she sat, Rosalind could see herself in the dressing table mirror. She looked at the reflection of a dispirited-looking woman with shapeless brown hair and a dreary cardigan. 'I don't think you need to worry. You probably wouldn't recognise me yourself,' she sighed, and then hesitated. 'Simon?'

'Yes?'

She could tell by the tone of his voice that his attention had wandered, and that he was reading, or had covered the handset to talk to someone in the room with him. She had wanted to ask if he thought she was beautiful, if he desired her, not just for her poise and her style but for herself. She wanted him to tell her that she wasn't the spoilt, selfish bitch that Michael thought her, that he had missed her. She wanted him to remind her that they could build on a mutual respect and liking and find happiness in a secure, successful marriage.

'It's nothing,' said Rosalind sadly. 'It doesn't matter.'

She cut the connection with her thumb and sat looking down at the phone for a long time. With an effort, she could push Michael's image aside and picture Simon instead. In his mid-forties, he was an attractive man, distinguished rather than handsome. Beneath the surface urbanity and sheen of success he was driven by ambition, but he could be a charming and witty companion and a considerate lover.

Lots of men compartmentalised their work lives and their private lives, Rosalind rationalised. It was stupid to feel upset when he shut her out. It wasn't as if she was marrying him for love. There were things she needed more than that.

But it would be nice to feel that he at least liked her, the way Michael liked Laura.

For some reason, Rosalind wanted to cry. The feeling stayed with her for the rest of the afternoon, but it only came to her later, as she bathed Jamie, that she hadn't thought about being stalked once all day. She sat back on her heels, testing the idea that she had spent a whole day without feeling tense or frightened. The awful creeping horror had been so much part of her life since the anonymous letters began that it was odd to think that it had lifted without her even noticing that it had gone.

She hadn't had time to worry about who might be following her, Rosalind admitted ruefully to herself as she lathered a flannel and scrubbed Jamie's neck, deaf to his protests. She had been too busy thinking about Michael and the muddled way he made her feel.

Rosalind didn't know why he confused her so much, why one minute he could make her feel blazingly angry and the next weak-kneed with the mere memory of his hands on her body, his lips on her skin. She wanted to be cool and poised, the way she normally was, not restless and cross and unsure of herself. Michael made her feel all of those things and more, but he also made her feel safe.

Safe. It was a wonderful feeling, one Rosalind had never appreciated until her world had been turned upside down by a nameless stranger, and she owed it to Michael. Because of him she could bathe Jamie without tensing every time she heard a telephone ring or a footstep outside. She could walk out of the door without wondering who was watching her. She could put Jamie to bed and not fear that he would somehow be gone in the morning.

She owed Michael all of that, and in return she had argued and complained and made exactly the kind of scenes he had always hated. Ashamed, Rosalind bit her lip and hung her head as she wrung out the flannel.

Michael, passing the door, saw her crouched by the edge of the bath. Her head was bent, her face partly hidden by her hair, and he braced himself against a painfully vivid memory of another time, another Rosalind, crouching to stroke a cat in the street, shaking back her silken tresses and then, in one of her quicksilver changes of mood, sliding an upward glance of her green, green eyes with their gleaming mixture of gaiety and pure seduction.

At that moment, Rosalind pushed back her hair and looked up just as she had done that day, but this time, Michael saw with a confused mixture of relief and regret, there was no mischief in her eyes, no provocative play of her long lashes. Instead, she looked tired and sad and oddly vulnerable.

He frowned. She had been absolutely impossible all day, snapping in the car, flouncing around the supermarket with her nose in the air, making bitchy comments about Laura Osborne, throwing her wealth and her precious fiancé in his face at every opportunity. Just when he let himself believe that she might have changed, she seemed to go out of her way to convince him that she was still the same spoilt beauty who had caused such havoc with his life before.

Michael had had quite enough of Rosalind for one day, he'd thought, but something in her expression made him stop, and before he had even realised what was happening his feet had carried him into the bathroom. 'What's the matter?' he found himself asking.

Rosalind pushed the brown hair wearily behind her ears. 'Oh…nothing.' Lifting Jamie out of the bath, she wrapped him in a big towel and cuddled him with mock fierceness until he squealed with pleasure.

'You didn't get any bad news about the stalker from Simon?' Michael persisted, even as he asked himself why he cared.

She sent him rather a puzzled look and shook her head. 'No, he didn't mention anything about it. Why?'

'I just thought you looked…worried about something.'

'No, I'm fine,' said Rosalind slowly. 'At least…' She hesitated. 'I need to talk to you, Michael. Can you wait until I've finished here?'

'All right,' he said, not knowing whether to be relieved or concerned by the change in her manner. He perched on the edge of the bath and picked up the plastic hippopotamus that had been keeping Jamie amused in the water. Opening the hippo's jaws, Michael found a tiny duck attached by a piece of elastic. He pulled it out experimentally, and released it. Feet paddling frantically, the duck was drawn inexorably back to the hippo who swallowed it in a final gulp.

Michael smiled ironically as he realised that it reminded him of all his attempts to forget Rosalind. He had been like the duck, going for as long as he could without thinking of her until a word or a look or a turn of the head would bring her image back so vividly that he knew that it had never really gone away at all. Her spell pulled him remorselessly back, no matter how hard he resisted, and the memories of her would swallow him up before he fought his way free of them once more. She was the hippo and he was the poor, doomed duck, destined never to get away.

When Jamie was dry and dressed in his pyjamas and a bright red dressing gown, Rosalind sat on the old nursing chair and wedged him between her knees so that she could comb his damp hair. He wriggled and protested, but Michael saw with an odd lack of surprise that, in spite of her lack of confidence on the childcare front, she could be firm enough when she wanted to. 'Why don't you go and find a book to read, Jamie?' she said at last with a final swipe of the comb. 'Then I'll dry your hair and we'll read a story.'

Trailing his dressing gown cord, Jamie escaped to his room, leaving a sudden silence behind in the bathroom.

Michael set the hippo back on the corner of the bath. 'What did you want to talk to me about?'

'I wanted to apologise,' said Rosalind. 'I've been behaving really badly ever since we left London and I'm sorry,' she finished in a rush.

For a moment Michael was too surprised to speak. 'What brought this on?' he asked eventually. This was a new Rosalind to him, and he wasn't quite sure how to deal with her.

Rosalind ran her hands through her hair in a tired gesture. 'I know I've been horrible all day,' she admitted. 'I was in a foul mood earlier, but when I'd calmed down a bit I did some thinking, and I realised that for the first time in months I hadn't spent the whole day looking over my shoulder and wondering who was watching me.'

She looked at him with eyes that were greener and more direct than he had ever seen them. 'I can't tell you what a relief it is, or what it means to know that Jamie is safe for a while, and I feel awful about being such a pain. I don't seem to have done anything but argue with you since we arrived, when I should have been thanking you for everything you've done for us.'

'It doesn't matter,' said Michael, feeling acutely uncomfortable. 'You've been under a lot of strain.'

'It's not just that.' She bent to pick up the towel and folded it very carefully on her lap, not looking at him. 'It's being with you again. You make me nervous.'

Rosalind, *nervous?* 'I don't mean to,' he said, taken aback.

'I know that. It's not anything you do.' She fidgeted with the edge of the towel. 'It's me. I've got myself in a state about being with you again,' she went on, with an honesty that staggered Michael. 'I keep thinking about the past and the things we did together and the awful way it all ended, and the more I think about it, the more tense I get.' She tried to smile, but it came out rather twisted. 'I feel like I'm still being stalked, only this time it's by memories instead of a stranger. I know it's stupid, I know anything between us was over a long time ago but...'

A blush of embarrassment crept up her cheeks as she trailed off, avoiding his eyes. 'I was really nervous about getting into bed with you last night,' she muttered.

'So was I,' Michael confessed.

Rosalind's head came up and she stared at him with such astonishment that Michael began to think he had put on a better show of unconcern than he had realised. 'Really?' she said huskily.

'Really. It's not easy negotiating around all the memories.'

'No,' she agreed. Her colour deepened, but she seemed determined to get it all off her chest now that she had started. 'Of course, I know that you're no more interested in another affair than I am, but I've been terrified that if I accidentally brushed against you, or was too relaxed with you, you might begin to suspect that I was trying to...you know...pretend things were like they were before.'

'I would never think that,' said Michael, amazed that the idea would even occur to Rosalind, whom he had always thought too self-absorbed to consider what anyone else might be feeling. 'As you say, we've both moved on,' he went on briskly. 'We've got different partners, different lives. It's an awkward situation, but no more than that.'

Rosalind seemed touchingly grateful for his matter-of-fact manner. 'Thank you,' she said. Clutching the towel to her chest, she got to her feet. 'I'm going to be good from now on,' she promised. 'You won't recognise me. I'll cook and I'll clean and I'll keep washing the dishes, and I won't complain about any of it.'

'And will you promise to be nice to Laura Osborne next time you see her?'

She squared her shoulders. 'Yes,' she said heroically.

'And let her give you some tips on improving your appearance?'

Rosalind hesitated, and then obviously realised that he was teasing her. 'I don't know if I can go *that* far,' she said, relaxing into a glinting smile that caught the breath in Michael's throat. 'But I won't be as rude as I was this afternoon, I promise.'

'That's good enough.' Michael got up from the bath, his answering smile fading as he looked at her. 'You're not the only one who needs to apologise, Rosalind. I've been in a filthy mood for the last two days, and I haven't been as sympathetic as I should have been. I'm sorry, too.' It was his turn to hesitate. 'I don't think either of us will be able to forget the past completely, but we could try and draw a line beneath it and start again.'

'I'd like that,' said Rosalind, with a tremulous smile.

There was a pause. Michael was aware that the air was charged with a kind of expectation, as if they should mark their agreement in some way. Should they shake hands? Kiss? The truth was that he didn't trust himself to touch her at all, in spite of all his brave talk about starting afresh.

In the end, he just stepped away from the door to let her pass. 'I'm glad we've cleared the air,' he said. 'Things should be easier now.'

CHAPTER SEVEN

IN MANY ways, things *were* easier after that. There were times over the next week when Rosalind felt as if she were living in a dream. She had stepped out of her own life into one which was quite different but which after only a few days seemed perfectly normal.

They soon fell into a routine. Jamie woke them in the morning and squeezed into the bed between them while they drank the tea Michael got up to make in the cold kitchen. Maud tended to sniff at that. She thought Michael spoilt Rosalind, but acknowledged that she did more than her fair share of the housework after such an indulged start to the day.

If anyone had told Rosalind a month earlier that she would be happy living in a house with virtually none of the modern conveniences that she took for granted in her own luxurious homes, Rosalind would have scoffed. She would have been incredulous at the idea that she could enjoy spending her days cooking and cleaning, but she began to catch herself humming as she worked, and she realised with a small shock that she *was* enjoying herself.

She liked not having to think too much. Instead of worrying about whether she had made a decision that would end up costing her father's company millions of pounds, she worried about whether the cake she'd daringly tried to bake would rise, or whether it would stay dry long enough to hang the washing out. The stalker was no more than a fading nightmare, as if part of a scary film she had once seen, and she no longer panicked the moment Jamie was out of her sight.

Safe, released from the claustrophobic cage of security that had trapped them in London, Jamie was having a wonderful time. He was firm friends with Tom Osborne, and between helping Rosalind cook, playing football with Michael, and breaking down Maud's defences, Jamie had no time to notice that there was no television. He adored Michael's aunt, who taught him how to play snap, read him stories and let him turn out her ancient and voluminous handbag.

Michael was working his way steadily through the chaos of papers in the study, but in the afternoons he would emerge to tackle the garden or kick a ball around with Jamie. Some days, the days Rosalind liked best, he explored the woods with them, and on the way home they would swing Jamie between them, high into the air. They looked like a family, they felt like a family, and it was all Rosalind could do sometimes to remember that they weren't a real family at all.

The days might be easy, but the nights were a different matter. The nights weren't easy at all. They were much, much more difficult. During the day, she and Michael could talk and laugh together, but as soon as the bedroom door closed behind them their conversation shrivelled and died in an atmosphere of unspoken and unacknowledged tension.

Sometimes Rosalind wished that they would argue again. Then she could go back to pretending that she disliked him instead of thinking about his hands and his mouth and how terribly, tantalisingly close he lay beside her. They were both very careful not to touch each other, but every time Michael stirred, every time he breathed, her senses tingled with the memory of how they had once made love.

Rosalind told herself that she was just being a dog in the manger. She had rejected the love Michael had offered her before, so she had no business to even *wonder* what it would be like if he wasn't committed to Kathy now. Desperately, she reminded herself of her own determination not to get involved in another messy relationship, but it didn't stop her heart lurching as Michael turned over, or her skin twitching at the nearness of his hard, male body.

No, the nights weren't easy at all.

'Oh, look, this is fabulous!' Rosalind lifted the dress from the trunk and held it up to admire. 'It looks like once of those dresses Grace Kelly used to wear in those old films.'

Having made the decision to move to a smaller house, Maud had reluctantly accepted that she would have to do something about the trunks of dresses and coats that she had kept for over fifty years. Rosalind was helping her, and the two women, who up to now had regarded each other with some wariness, had discovered a shared enthusiasm for clothes and were now getting on like a house on fire, if not making a lot of progress in deciding what to throw away.

Maud sighed nostalgically. 'I wore that to cocktail parties in the Fifties, with pearls and gloves,' she told Rosalind. 'I was much slimmer then, as you've probably guessed.'

'I bet you looked wonderful in it too, didn't you?'

'Oh, my dear, it's all so long ago now.' Maud shook her head and then relented. 'But John used to say that I did.' Her beaky face softened. 'That was his favourite dress. I used to wear it all the time because he liked it so much.'

Rosalind lowered the dress. Maud was such an intimidating figure that it was hard to imagine her anxious to please anyone. Her husband must have been quite a character. 'What was he like?' she asked curiously.

'John? He was rather like Michael. Quiet, competent, clever.' Maud smiled reminiscently. 'People used to wonder what I saw in him. He wasn't at all handsome, but when he was in the room I never saw anyone else. Do you know what I mean?'

Rosalind thought about Michael, about the line of his jaw and the set of his mouth and the way everything seemed sharper and more clear when he was near. 'Yes, I know what you mean,' she said slowly, and Maud nodded.

'Of course you do,' she said.

Looking into Maud's sharp eyes, Rosalind saw the understanding there and a faint flush stained her cheeks. Michael's aunt saw a little too much for comfort. 'I hope you're not going to throw this dress away,' she said, turning away. 'It's so special.'

'Why don't you try it on, if you like it that much?'

'*Could* I?' Rosalind lit up at the chance to wear something feminine and flattering for a change, and she pirouetted in front of the mirror, smoothing the material over her hips. 'I love it!'

'It certainly suits you,' said Maud. 'Wait, I might even have the pearls somewhere.' She dug around in a box on the dressing table and held up a necklace of beautifully matched pearls. 'Put this on.'

The pearls set off the dress to perfection. There was no doubt that it was a period piece, with its ankle-length, figure-hugging skirt in deep green lamé and its simple bodice and long sleeves of a paler green crêpe, but it looked stunning on Rosalind.

'It might have been made for you,' said Maud, studying her critically. 'Why don't you wear it for the drinks party on Friday?'

'Won't I be a bit overdressed?'

'The great thing about a dress like that, Rosalind, is that if you wear it with the right style you'll make everyone else look *under*dressed.'

'I can't imagine Laura Osborne ever looking underdressed,' said Rosalind, before she could help herself, and Maud's eyes met hers in the mirror with amused understanding.

'She will if you wear that.'

'You're not really going to wear that, are you?' said Michael that Friday as he watched Rosalind wriggling into Maud's cocktail dress.

'Don't you like it?' she said, settling it on her shoulders.

Michael wasn't sure whether he liked it or not. He had grown used to the new Rosalind, who ran around the house in leggings and a sweatshirt, a Rosalind whose plain brown hair blew around in the wind and who had smudges of flour on her face when she made scones. A Rosalind who lay beside him every night with cool satin slipping over her skin.

She looked beautiful tonight. She looked like the old Rosalind. Perhaps it was just as well, thought Michael. It was too easy to forget that she was still the same girl.

'I think it might be a bit much for drinks, that's all,' he said. 'It's not going to be a formal occasion.'

'I know,' said Rosalind, 'but I think Maud would like me to wear it. Besides,' she added as she sat down at the dressing table, 'I haven't got anything else to wear. The only skirt I've got is that horrible brown thing, and it's dirty.'

Placing the pearls around her neck, she bent her head forward and shook her hair out of the way so that she could fasten the clasp. The soft, vulnerable nape exposed made something ache sharply inside Michael, and he turned abruptly away to find a tie.

When he looked back, Rosalind was leaning into the mirror, her vivid face intent as she put on her lipstick, and without warning Michael was submerged in a wash of memory. Time slipped, and he saw another Rosalind, tumbled copper hair cascading down her back, putting on her make-up with exactly the same expression of concentration. He had taken her to a hotel in Cornwall for a weekend. It hadn't been the kind of five-star hotel she was used to, but it had been the best he could afford. The atmosphere had been anonymous, the décor faintly shabby, the food disappointing, but it hadn't mattered, not then.

They had spent the afternoon in bed. Michael could still feel the satiny warmth of her skin beneath his hands, could feel his blood surging with the wild, exhilarating passion that had had them both ensnared. Afterwards, Rosalind had covered him with soft, enticing kisses. He remembered her smiling wickedly, remembered the teasing promises she had murmured into his throat, remembered the feel of her hair trailing over his body.

Later still, they had decided they were hungry. They'd dressed for dinner, just as they were doing now. He remembered exactly what she had been wearing: a slinky black dress that had left her back tantalisingly bare. He had been watching her put on her lipstick, chattering gaily, when their eyes had met in the mirror and the words had died on her lips. She'd put her lipstick down and turned. Without a word, she had walked over to him and carefully unbuttoned his shirt.

They never had gone down for dinner, Michael remembered.

He tried to concentrate on doing up the cuffs of his shirt, but he couldn't take his eyes off Rosalind as she sat at the dressing table in Maud's old dress. She had left the fragile zip undone until the last moment, so that the dress gaped open slightly, and he could see the line of her back and a tantalising glimpse of honey-coloured skin. Slowly, drawn by some irresistible force outside him, Michael's eyes travelled up her spine, up to where her hair swung softly against the nape of her neck, and moved on with a sickening sense of inevitability to lock with Rosalind's green gaze in the mirror.

They stared at each other while the air evaporated between them and the silence reverberated with the thunderous boom of his heart. Michael's mouth was dry. He couldn't move, couldn't speak, could just stand there like a fool, enmeshed in her eyes. It was an enormous relief when Rosalind put down her lipstick with a sharp click and stood up.

'Can you zip me up?' she said, presenting her back to him. Her voice was a little husky, but otherwise she seemed to be intent on pretending that everything was normal.

Michael hesitated, torn between the longing to touch her and the humiliating fear that he would not be able to control himself if he did. He looked at Rosalind's back and his body thumped with a kind of despair at finding himself sucked back under her spell.

'Michael?' There was a faint note of enquiry in Rosalind's voice as she glanced over her shoulder, and

Michael squared his shoulders. He could hardly refuse, and anyway, what was there to be afraid of? All he had to do was pull up her zip and step away. Easy.

Bracing himself, he stepped over and took the zip between his fingers. With his other hand he held the dress steady at the base of her spine. He could feel the heavy texture of the material, the cold metal of the zip against his fingertips, could smell her clean, soft hair and her perfume, and the scent of her skin, and his senses reeled. Michael swallowed and set his jaw as he pulled the zip smoothly upwards, watching mesmerised as it closed over the smooth golden back. At the top his fingers encountered a hook and eye, and he fastened them together, his fingers grazing the nape of her neck.

Now was the moment for him to step away.

Now was the moment for her to step away, Rosalind told herself. She had felt so different when she'd first put the dress on. Its flattering lines and subtle glamour made her feel much more like her old self, and she had sat down at the dressing table determined to prove that she was more than a match for Laura Osborne, who was still on far too friendly terms with Michael as far as Rosalind was concerned.

All she needed, Rosalind had thought, was some lipstick. But as she'd leant closer to the mirror she had found herself distracted by Michael's reflection as he moved around the room behind her. He wore a pale yellow shirt with a grey patterned tie knotted loosely around his neck, and his expression had been strained as he'd fastened his cuffs. Rosalind's eyes had rested on his deft brown fingers and all at once she'd been swamped by a wash of desire that had blotted out all thoughts of the party, of Laura, or the effect of her dress, and left her with nothing but an awareness of Michael so intense that she'd almost been able to feel the texture of his skin and the compact strength of his body and the warmth of his mouth.

Rosalind had fought the sensation, appalled at what was happening to her. Hadn't she just decided that she was her old, assured, invulnerable self again? Rosalind Leigh didn't dissolve at the mere sight of a preoccupied-looking man doing up his shirt. Her heart didn't ricochet around her chest and her legs didn't turn to cotton wool, and her breathing always stayed perfectly normal. Rosalind Leigh was cool and composed and completely in control.

To prove it to herself, Rosalind had torn her eyes away from Michael's and somehow managed to stand up. She had been proud of the unconcerned way she had asked him to do up her zip, but it had been a mistake. The warm brush of his fingers had sent a slow shudder down her spine, and the longing to lean back into the hard body behind her had been so acute that she'd closed her eyes.

Michael's hands were still on the fastening. All she had to do was thank him and move away, but Rosalind couldn't move. She waited for Michael to drop his hands, but it was as if they were both poised on the brink of a dizzying drop, reluctant to step forward and unable to step back.

Rosalind never knew how long they stood there, suspended in time, but at the very moment she could bear it no longer Michael let out a breath, and with a shattering sense of release she felt his hands drop onto her shoulders and spread, curving around her throat so that his fingers could trace the line of collarbone under the fine crêpe. Hardly daring to breathe, Rosalind stood taut and trembling as his palms drifted on to smooth lingeringly, lovingly, down her arms.

Her heart was beating in her throat, and she opened her eyes wide as she fought against the drumming need to succumb to the sheer seduction of his touch, but it was no good. Reeled in by some invisible force, Rosalind turned between his hands. She didn't think about what she was doing. She didn't want to think. She just knew that she had to turn.

They were standing very close, barely a heartbeat apart. Very slowly, Rosalind lifted her eyes and looked into his for a timeless moment. There was no need to say anything. Then Michael's gaze dropped to her mouth, and inside her something twisted, deep and urgent. With a delicious, agonising, taunting lack of haste, he let his hands travel back up her arms and over the curve of her shoulders to cradle her jaw between strong, warm fingers.

'Rosalind,' he said, and his deep voice reverberated through her. 'Do you remember that hotel in Cornwall?'

'Yes,' she said with difficulty, 'I remember.'

'Do you remember changing for dinner?'

'Yes,' she breathed, and his tantalising thumbs caressed her cheek.

'We were going to go out,' Michael went on, without taking his eyes from her mouth, 'but you turned. You walked over to me, you told me you weren't hungry any more. Do you remember that?'

Rosalind nodded. 'I unbuttoned your shirt,' she reminded him in a whisper, her hands lifting as if of their own volition to begin slowly unfastening the yellow shirt as she had done before. 'And then you kissed me.'

Michael drew a sharp breath. 'Can I kiss you again,

Rosalind?' he asked, his mouth very close to her own, and she closed her eyes in an agony of anticipation.

'Yes…' She let herself lean into him at last. 'Yes…please kiss me.'

And then the waiting was over, and his lips came down on hers with a jolt of intense, electric delight. Rosalind melted into him as past and present spun together. Somewhere deep inside she knew that this was what she had been thinking about ever since she had walked into Emma's sitting room and seen Michael standing by the window. It was what she had been dreaming about ever since he had walked out of her life and left her to the bleakness of discovering that she had thrown away something irreplaceable.

But now Michael was kissing her again, and Rosalind abandoned herself to the dizzying rush of sensation. It was so good to be able to wrap her arms around him, to touch him and taste him and dissolve beneath the intoxicating exploration of his lips. Even remembering as she did how it had been before, Rosalind was unprepared for the speed with which the kiss ran out of control. It was wildfire, crackling along her veins, feeding on the terrible tension that had simmered between them for the last ten days until it rocketed between them, leaping the last few, unregretted barriers of restraint. They kissed and kissed again, and again, deep, hungry, almost frantic kisses that held all the pent-up frustration of the nights spent lying so carefully apart.

Desperately, Rosalind pressed closer, fumbling with the last button of his shirt until she could push it aside and slide her arms around him. The feel of his tautly muscled body made her gasp with pleasure, and Michael smiled, murmuring her name against her throat.

'Rosalind…Rosalind, I've been thinking about this all week…'

'I know, I know…' She kissed his bare chest and thrilled at Michael's shudder of response.

'Rosalind,' he said raggedly, and pulled her over to the bed, unhooking her dress and feeling for the zip he had pulled up so agonisingly only minutes before as they went.

They had forgotten Maud, forgotten the party, forgotten everything but the fire consuming them. But Maud had not forgotten them, and even as Rosalind gasped Michael's name as they fell, still kissing, onto the bed, it was echoed outside the door.

'Michael?' Maud knocked imperatively. 'Rosalind? Are you nearly ready? It's almost half past seven and those ghastly Pearsons are always on time.'

Inside the bedroom, there was a jarring silence. Breathless, tangled together, Rosalind and Michael had frozen at her knock, too shocked by the intrusion of reality to move.

'Michael?' Puzzled by the lack of response, Maud knocked again.

'We'll be down in a minute,' Michael managed to call back at last. His voice sounded hoarse and strained, but Maud didn't seem to notice.

'I'll be in the sitting room,' she said through the door, and they heard her making her way stiffly down the stairs.

For a moment, they lay staring at each other, then Michael sat up. Resting his elbows on his knees, he raked his fingers through his hair and swore.

'I couldn't have put it better myself,' said Rosalind shakily, pulling herself up to sit beside him.

Michael sat hunched forward, his head in his hands.

'I'm sorry,' he said in a flat voice. He didn't look at Rosalind. 'That was my fault.'

'It was my fault too,' she said. 'I could have stepped away. I didn't have to turn.'

He glanced up at that, eyes suddenly alert. 'Why did you?'

Skewered by the pale grey gaze, Rosalind swallowed. 'You know why,' she said, hoping that she sounded cooler than she felt. 'There was always a chemistry between us, and it's still there, whether we like it or not. The question is, what do we do about it?'

'We could ignore it,' said Michael.

Biting her lip, Rosalind turned to hide a sudden, humiliated flush. She might want to impress him with her coolness, but there was no need for him to make it quite so obvious that he could just forget what had happened!

'Or...' he went on, and she looked back quickly to see a gleam in the grey eyes. He had seen the flash of sickening disappointment in her face, thought Rosalind, but when his expression was alight with the teasing laughter that melted her bones it somehow didn't matter.

'Or?' she prompted, a smile trembling on her lips.

'Or—if we wanted to—we could give in and let the chemistry take over.'

'If we wanted to,' Rosalind agreed.

They seemed to be having two conversations. One was straight-faced, with an undercurrent of amusement, but the conversation they held with their eyes was warm with promise and the knowledge of what they both wanted.

Michael opened his mouth to speak, only to be interrupted by the ring of the doorbell. The next moment, what sounded like a great crowd of people filled the hall, their voices echoing up the stairs. Michael cursed softly under his breath. 'We'll have to talk about this later,' he said, and stood up reluctantly. 'I'd better go down.'

His fingers were warm and strong around Rosalind's hand as he helped her to her feet. She wanted to cling to it, to tell him to ignore the party and to pull him back down onto the bed, but instead she drew a steadying breath and even managed a smile. 'You'll have to do me up again, I think.'

Michael's answering smile was rather twisted as he pulled up the zip of her dress once more and refastened the hook before refastening his shirt. Rosalind watched as he stuffed it into his trousers and straightened his tie.

'You've got lipstick on your face,' she said, wiping a smear from his jaw with her thumb, which tingled at the graze of rough male skin. Beneath the dull thud of frustration, she was conscious of anticipation fluttering into life at the thought of the night ahead. They just had to get through the evening, and then…oh, *then*…

'Are you OK?' Michael laid his palm against her cheek and looked down at her with concern in his eyes.

Rosalind nodded. 'I'm fine. Just give me a minute.'

'I'll see you downstairs, then.'

When he had gone, she sank onto the dressing table stool and looked at her dishevelled reflection. Was it only minutes ago that she had sat here and congratulated herself on regaining her normal cool composure? There was nothing cool or composed about the girl who looked back at her from the mirror. She was glowing, almost luminous, with dark, languorous eyes, tousled hair and a mouth still trembling from Michael's kisses.

She looked as if she were in love. The thought slipped unbidden into Rosalind's mind, and she frowned slightly. She could admit now that what she felt for Michael was stronger than she had been prepared to accept before, but it wasn't love. It was just an intense physical attraction, more than she had ever known for anyone else, but still not love. She wasn't going to get herself involved in *that.* She was just going to enjoy the chemistry. Her body might be in thrall to Michael, but she was keeping her heart firmly to herself.

Reassured, Rosalind brushed her hair, reapplied her lipstick and went down to meet Maud's guests.

The party seemed interminable. Rosalind smiled and nodded and agreed that, yes, it had been a very cold April, but all the time she was preternaturally aware of every move Michael made. He was circulating, refilling glasses, shaking hands, keeping the conversation going—doing exactly what she was normally so good at, in fact.

Tonight, though, her social skills had deserted her. She couldn't concentrate when her body was booming with anticipation of the night ahead. She kept catching glimpses of his smile, or the way he turned his head, and every time her stomach would clench with longing. She couldn't wait for everyone to go.

'All right?' Michael came up behind her and rested his hand against the small of her back. It was a casual gesture, familiar rather than intimate, but desire shuddered down Rosalind's spine, and the need to turn and press her face into his throat was so intense that she flinched and closed her eyes briefly, as if from a pain.

Opening them, she found herself looking straight at a neighbour Maud had introduced as Sue. Certain from the other woman's expression that she had seen the naked desire in her face, Rosalind flushed and averted her eyes.

'Sorry, was I staring?' To her surprise, it was Sue who seemed flustered. 'I've been trying to work out who you remind me of. I'm sure I've seen you somewhere before.' Her words fell into a lull in the conversation, and everyone turned to look at Rosalind. 'This is your first visit up here, isn't it?'

'What? Oh...yes,' said Rosalind, still too aware of Michael's warm hand on her back to pay much attention.

'Now you come to mention, she does look vaguely familiar,' said another guest. 'You're not thinking of an actress?'

'I know who it is,' said Laura, joining in the conversation, and Rosalind snapped abruptly out of her dream where everyone vanished and Michael carried her back up to the bedroom. 'I had a feeling I'd seen you before, too. Has anyone ever told you you look a bit like Rosalind Leigh?'

Rosalind tensed under the scrutiny of at least fifteen pairs of eyes, intensely grateful for the arm Michael slipped reassuringly around her waist.

'Rosalind Leigh?' said Maud, baffled. 'Who on earth is she?'

'Gerald Leigh's daughter,' a man whose name Rosalind hadn't caught informed Maud. 'You know, the tycoon who was killed in a helicopter crash last year. Gave the stock market the jitters for a day or two.'

When Maud continued to look blank, his wife intervened. 'His daughter is one of these semi-celebrities. She doesn't seem to do anything but go to parties and get herself photographed. She's always in the gossip pages of glossy magazines.'

Michael's arm tightened around Rosalind as he drew her closer for support. 'You haven't been leading a double life, have you, darling?'

'It seems as if I must have been,' said Rosalind, horribly conscious of her ghastly fixed smile. Her voice sounded so hollow that she waited for a row of accusing fingers to point at her, but instead there was general laughter.

'I don't think she looks anything like Rosalind Leigh,' someone else objected. 'You just think that because of her having the same name. Rosalind Leigh's got that amazing hair. There were lots of pictures of her in the papers when her engagement to Simon Hungerford was announced.'

'That's true,' her neighbour agreed. 'And she's always fabulously dressed. Not that there's anything wrong with your clothes, Rosalind,' she added hastily, 'but you obviously have to operate on the same budget as the rest of us, unlike that Rosalind Leigh.' She sighed enviously. 'It's all right for some. We could all look stunning if we had that kind of money.'

'Ah, but would you be happy? No, seriously,' Sue went on. 'I often wonder how much fun it is to be that rich. I mean, Rosalind Leigh's a beautiful girl, but what else is she? It must be a pretty superficial existence when you think about it. She doesn't *do* anything. I'll bet she's never done a hand's turn in her life!'

Rosalind thought of the cooking and the cleaning and the washing up that she had done since she had arrived in Yorkshire, and her fingers clenched around her glass. Her jaw was rigid with the effort of keeping her smile in place.

'Those kind of people don't have to,' said her friend, with all the authority of a regular reader of the gossip columns. 'They've got no idea what it's like in the real world. They're so arrogant they think that the rules don't apply to them. What gets me is the way they always look so smug and superior. Take this Rosalind Leigh—what's she ever done other than spend a lot of money and go to a lot of parties? She probably hasn't got two brain cells to rub together.'

The woman standing next to her was nodding. 'I always think she looks hard as nails. I've heard she's a real bitch.'

'I think she looks rather sad,' Laura put in unexpectedly. 'Not like you,' she added to Rosalind, with a smile. 'I didn't mean that you looked exactly like Rosalind Leigh. It just seemed to me that there was a resemblance, especially in that wonderful dress.'

'It's Maud's,' said Rosalind, seizing gratefully on the chance to change the subject, but the rest of the party were still intent on tearing her character to shreds. Afraid that it would look as if Michael was protecting her, she moved out of the comforting circle of his arm and talked to Laura about clothes with a kind of desperate animation, but behind her she could hear that they had moved on to her engagement.

'Did you see the pictures when she and Simon Hungerford announced their engagement? Talk about pleased with themselves!'

'God, yes! They looked insufferable, didn't they? Mind you, they're well matched. I should think they're both as ruthless as each other when it comes to getting their own way.'

'That makes them sound too interesting,' put in another voice. 'I've never seen this Rosalind Leigh, but she's probably just a boring little socialite. And as for Simon Hungerford, he's a typical politician.'

There was an immediate chorus of agreement. 'Loathsome man! I can't stand the way he talks down to people!'

'He's such a slimeball!'

'I wouldn't trust him further than I could throw him.'

Rosalind could feel Michael's anxious eyes on her as she chatted feverishly to Laura while the group behind her sanctimoniously recycled gossip they had read. They were fine ones to talk about her being smug, Rosalind thought bitterly. Now they had moved on to her father. 'Of course, I always thought there was something fishy about the way Gerald Leigh died,' someone said, and she flinched. She didn't think she could bear much more.

Michael had obviously decided that it was time to change the conversation too. He broke into the circle and insisted on filling up everyone's glass. 'Does anyone know of a good estate agent?' he asked, and to Rosalind's intense relief the diversion worked like a charm. Abandoning gossip, Maud's neighbours leapt on a subject even closer to their hearts. Working out the price of their properties kept them occupied for a good half hour, and by the time the rival merits of the local estate agents had been thrashed out, complete with horror stories about buying/selling, the elusive resemblance between Michael Brooke's wife and the despised Rosalind Leigh had been forgotten.

CHAPTER EIGHT

'I THOUGHT those two were never going to go,' said Michael, coming back into the sitting room after seeing out the last of the stragglers. He paused, watching Rosalind, who was collecting glasses with stiff, jerky movements. 'Maud's gone to bed,' he said carefully.

'Good,' said Rosalind. 'She must be tired.'

'Yes.'

'Still, she enjoyed the party,' Rosalind went on brightly.

'It's more than I did,' said Michael. He hesitated. 'Are you all right?'

'I'm fine.' She flashed him a brittle smile and the glasses chinked together in her hands as she loaded them onto a tray.

Michael picked up a couple of glasses from the mantelpiece. 'I'm sorry about what happened. It can't have been very comfortable having to stand there while everyone talked about you like that.'

'It was quite an eye-opener, wasn't it?' said Rosalind lightly. She was determined not to admit how hurt she had been, but inside she felt humiliated, slightly sick. *Arrogant. Selfish. Vain. Superficial. Stupid.* The words hammered in Rosalind's brain. Was that really how people thought of her? Was that how she *was*? 'Funny how they didn't recognise me, in spite of knowing so much about me!' she added, unable to prevent the hurt breaking through.

'They don't know anything about you, Rosalind,'

Michael said, but the sympathy in his eyes caught her on the raw.

'You should have joined in, Michael,' she said bitterly, emptying bowls of leftover nuts with ferocious concentration. 'They would have loved to have heard what *you* had to say. You could have told them just what a bitch I am. They would have lapped it up!'

Michael shook his head. 'I wouldn't say anything like that about you.'

'You did before!'

'We all say things we don't mean when we're angry, Rosalind,' he said steadily. 'It's true that I've thought some pretty bitter things about you over the last five years, but since we've been here you've proved me wrong. No one who'd seen the way you've worked this last week, or the way you are with Jamie and Maud, could accuse you of being lazy or selfish now.'

'They might strike *lazy* off the list,' she allowed in a tight, hard voice. 'But that would still leave me as smug, superficial, boring and...what was it again?' she pretended to search her memory. 'Oh, yes, hard as nails!'

Her eyes were shimmering with hurt, angry tears, but she wouldn't let herself cry. Michael sighed as he looked at her pinched face and the two hectic spots of colour on her cheeks. 'They were just people who've seen your picture in a magazine and envy you your money,' he said, as if picking his words carefully. 'You shouldn't care what they think.'

'I don't care!' snapped Rosalind, crashing bowls together, and then her hands stilled and her shoulders slumped. 'Oh, all right, yes, I do. I do mind.'

'The Rosalind Leigh they were talking about wouldn't give a damn,' he said, 'so you see, you're not the same person. They weren't talking about the real you.'

Rosalind looked down at the bowls in her hand. 'I don't know who the real me is any more,' she said sadly. 'I'm not sure if I've ever known.'

'I do.' Removing the bowls from her numb grasp and setting them aside, Michael took her by the waist. 'The real Rosalind is the girl I was kissing earlier this evening.' His voice was very deep. 'Leave these things and come to bed, Rosalind. I'll remind you what the real you is like.'

Rosalind closed her eyes. The temptation to sway towards him was overwhelming. He was so close. All she had to do was slide her arms around his neck and kiss him. 'Michael, I can't,' she said.

Michael drew her closer, bent his head to kiss her neck. 'Why not?' he murmured, and Rosalind opened her eyes wide as a shudder of sheer desire snaked through her at the warm touch of his lips.

'I'm engaged to Simon,' she said hopelessly.

Michael's lips stilled, and he lifted his head to look into her eyes that were dark with desire and regret. 'You were engaged when we kissed earlier this evening and it didn't seem to matter then,' he reminded her.

'I know.' Rosalind met his gaze steadily. 'And it's true that if Maud hadn't interrupted us we would have made love and it would have been wonderful. I'm not pretending I didn't want that.'

'You still do want that,' said Michael. 'Or are you going to try and tell me that the chemistry has gone?'

'No.' She shook her head. 'The chemistry's still there—but so is Simon. He's my fiancé, and I'd forgotten all about him,' she said, ashamed. 'There isn't any excuse, but I've felt like a different person since I've been here, Michael. My life in London has seemed so remote, as if it belongs to someone else, but those people tonight reminded me who I am. I *am* the Rosalind Leigh they were talking about, and I can't sleep with you when I'm engaged to be married to another man.'

Michael let her go. 'You told me you didn't love Simon,' he said, with an edge of bitterness.

'I don't.'

'Why does it suddenly make such a difference, then?' he asked. 'We're not talking about getting involved with emotions, or anything else that would affect your engagement. We both know that there's no future in what we've got between us, but we're here, we're alone, and I think it's too late to pretend that we don't want each other.'

His hands reached for Rosalind once more and he drew her back towards him. 'Why not just accept the chemistry and make the most of the time we've got together?' he said, his voice very deep and tempting. 'Your engagement's part of your other life; you said as much yourself. What we've got is a physical thing. It won't hurt anybody. It's just...'

'Sex?' suggested Rosalind in a flat voice, and Michael's hands fell from her waist.

'That was all you wanted it to be before,' he reminded her, and she flushed.

'It was different then.' Moving away before she gave in to the terrible temptation he offered, Rosalind sat down on the edge of an armchair and pressed the heels of her hands against her eyes. 'Please try to understand, Michael. I may not love Simon, but I do respect him, and he deserves my loyalty. I made an agreement with him and I have to stick by it. You can see that, can't you?'

'Well, since you ask, no, I can't,' said Michael bitterly. 'I don't understand why a girl who has everything wants to throw her life away by marrying a man she doesn't even pretend to love.'

'Perhaps I'm just a spoilt, stupid socialite who wants to get her picture in the paper,' Rosalind offered, lowering her hands wearily from her face.

'No.' He sat down heavily in a chair opposite her. 'That's not why. Why *are* you marrying him, Rosalind? You've said he doesn't love you, so what can Simon possibly offer you that you don't already have?'

'You wouldn't understand,' she said dispiritedly.

'Try me.'

Rosalind rested her head against the back of the chair. She felt very tired. 'Simon can give me security.'

'Security?' echoed Michael. 'You've got more money than most people ever dream of. How can you possibly need security?'

'I'm not talking about financial security,' she said, looking down at her hands. 'I need a different kind of security. I want the security of being Simon's wife, of having a proper role, an identity of some kind.'

'But Rosalind, you *have* an identity,' said Michael, uncomprehending. 'You're Rosalind Leigh.'

'Yes, I'm rich Rosalind Leigh, and that's how everyone thinks of me. I want to stop wondering every time I meet a man what exactly he wants from me.' She sighed. 'I can't tell you how many times I've been out with guys who are charming and funny and good-looking, who are very good at making me feel that they like me for myself, and then I find out that while they think my green eyes are quite attractive, they're not nearly as seductive as my bank balance.'

Michael was frowning. 'You don't really believe that men are only interested in you for your money, do you?'

'I've learnt to believe it the hard way,' said Rosalind.

'I'm tired of being disappointed, Michael, tired of hoping that *this* one will be different.'

'*I* was different,' said Michael. 'Or did you think I was after your money as well?'

She shook her head. 'No, I never thought that of you. That's one of the reasons I enjoyed being with you so much. But...'

'But what?'

'But you liked my body more than you liked me, just like other men liked my money more.' Rosalind sighed slightly. 'Perhaps I'm just not a very likeable person. Anyway,' she went on, before Michael could speak, 'I've given up waiting for a man who'll like me for myself. I'm taking my father's advice. He always said that my mother had only married him for his money, and he didn't want me to make the same mistakes that he had. He told me to stick to men who were as wealthy as I was, and then at least I'd know they weren't looking for a way to get rich quick.'

'So you're marrying Simon Hungerford for *his* money?' said Michael tonelessly.

'In a way. There are other things I want, as well as security. I desperately need someone I can trust to help me deal with the companies I've inherited from my father. I've got financial advisers, of course, but it's all so complicated. I'm tired of struggling to make sense of it all on my own. I want someone who'll take the responsibility off my shoulders and look out for my interests without being paid to do it. Simon will do that. He understands how companies like my father's work.'

Michael's expression was sardonic, and she hurried on, wanting him to understand. 'It's not just that, of course. I like Simon, I admire him. He's clever and charming and successful. We complement each other in lots of ways. But, most importantly of all, Simon understands what it's like for me. He knows what I want out of the marriage, and it suits him very well too.'

'What does *he* get out of it?'

Rosalind lifted her shoulders. 'A political hostess. Someone with the right connections who will say and do the right things and won't demand too much attention from him. It's not a very romantic arrangement,' she said, meeting Michael's eyes defensively, 'but I won't be the first woman to settle for security. I've never believed in true love, or any of that stuff. It seems to me that love doesn't last, but the arrangement Simon and I have will. I'll be the perfect political wife, and in return I'll have a secure life and a stable base for Jamie.'

Michael's expression was unconvinced. 'Do you think that will be enough to make you happy, Rosalind?' he asked, and her eyes slid away from his. She didn't answer immediately.

'I think I'll be content,' she said at last. 'I'm going to keep my side of the bargain. I may not believe in love, but I do believe in loyalty, and that's why I can't sleep with you, even though I want to.'

There was a long pause. 'So you're going to ignore the chemistry between us after all?' said Michael.

'Yes.'

He leant forward in his chair, his eyes on her face. 'Do you think that's going to be easy, Rosalind?' he asked, and she swallowed.

'No, but I'm going to try.' She made herself meet his gaze. 'We should both try, and not just for Simon's sake. There's Kathy to think about, too. You seem to have forgotten her.'

The light eyes flickered. 'You're right,' he said. 'I had.'

They finished washing the glasses in silence and then, because there was nowhere else to go, they went to bed. Rosalind lay rigidly, her body raging, and wondered why the right decision was so often the hardest one. But it *had* been the right one. It was no good saying that Simon need never know, as an insistent inner voice had been pointing out. That wasn't the point. *She* would know. She had chosen to marry Simon, and she owed it to him and to herself to make the best she could of their marriage. What kind of wife would she be if she gave in to the temptation racking her right now?

Marriage with Simon might not be ideal, but it was her best chance of finding the security and contentment she craved. He didn't make her feel the way Michael did, but, as she and Michael had discovered before, sexual attraction wasn't enough. She and Simon were compatible in other, more important ways.

But it didn't stop her wishing that she hadn't been so brutally reminded of where her loyalties lay. If Maud's neighbours had only stuck to the weather, or the flagrant breach of planning regulations at the new house down the road, she would have been in Michael's arms instead of spending yet another night clinging miserably to the edge of the bed.

'I'm sorry,' she said, subdued, into the darkness, knowing that Michael would understand what she meant.

'Don't be.' Beside her, Michael had been trying to tell himself that it was just as well that things had turned out as they had. It had been all very well to talk about not getting involved, about the chemistry of mere physical attraction, but it would be easy—much too easy—to fall in love with her all over again.

Nothing had changed. He might understand rather better why Rosalind was so chary of letting anyone too close, but all that talk of financial deals and the corporate complexities Simon Hungerford was to deal with had only underlined how different their lives were, and how different their lives would remain. Far better to stick with the fiction about his relationship with Kathy to salve his pride, and not let himself get any more involved than he was already. It would only end in bitterness and tears, as it had done before.

'It's probably for the best,' he added, but it wasn't much comfort.

'I'm going to get some milk.' Rosalind found Michael in the garden, where he was savagely hacking at an overgrown buddleia. 'Can you keep an eye on Jamie?'

He lowered the saw and nodded. 'OK.'

'I won't be a minute.'

'Fine.'

All their conversations were like that now: careful, stilted, excruciatingly polite. It had been four days since the party: four days when Rosalind had done her best to forget the kiss and the passion it had unleashed, and three nights when she had lain next to Michael and known that it was impossible.

It wasn't even as if Michael was making things difficult, she thought as she walked across the green to the village shop. They hadn't talked about the kiss, or the tension that still simmered between them again. They hadn't talked about anything. They had just got on with their jobs and pretended that nothing had happened.

The shop was empty. Rosalind took some milk from the cool cabinet and made her way to the counter. Searching through her purse for some change, she glanced incuriously at the newspapers spread out by the till and stopped dead in shocked recognition. Money forgotten in her hand, she stared down at the headlines splashed across every paper, from tabloid to broadsheet.

MP EMBROILED IN SEX SCANDAL
HUNGERFORD RESISTS CALLS FOR RESIGNATION
MY NIGHTS WITH SEXY SIMON BY LUSCIOUS LYDIA

In disbelief, Rosalind's eyes travelled over the various photographs of Simon. One or two of the papers used his official photograph, as an MP, but most showed him running the gauntlet of a mob of reporters, hand held up against the flash of cameras, while the tabloids had juxtaposed him with pictures of a girl modelling a bikini in a provocative pose.

Misinterpreting her horrified expression, Mrs Ruddock leant over the counter. 'Load of hypocrites, that's what I say,' she said comfortably. 'These MPs think they can get away with anything. I feel sorry for their families. They never think of them, do they?'

'No,' said Rosalind dully. 'No, they don't.'

She felt blank, icy with shock. As if watching someone else, she saw herself hand over a five-pound note. 'I'll take a newspaper as well, please, Mrs Ruddock,' she said, and marvelled with a detached part of her mind at how calm she sounded.

Somehow, she managed to get outside the shop, and stood staring blindly around her. She wanted to run and hide somewhere, but where could she go? If she took the paper back to the house, Michael might see it, and Rosalind didn't think she could bear that.

In the end, she sat on a bench overlooking the green and opened up the paper with a sick feeling of dread at what she was going to read. It was the old sordid story. Simon had been seen in a nightclub with the girl, called Lydia, who was described as a model. He had huffed and puffed and denied any relationship, only to discover that she had been persuaded to tell all to one of the tabloids, obligingly providing incriminating photographs while she was at it. Simon was still trying to bluff it out on the grounds that he was single, but the paper remarked upon the absence of his fiancée, daughter of the late Gerald Leigh, who had yet to appear and stand by her man, as was traditional in the circumstances.

Rosalind put the paper into the bin beside her. The last thing she wanted was to talk to Simon, but she supposed that in all fairness she should give him the chance to put his side of the story. Still with the same sickening sense of unreality, she walked over to the phone box on the other side of the green and counted out some coins. Then, drawing a deep breath, she rang Simon's private line.

She had half hoped that he wouldn't be there, but he was, and in a blustering, defensive mood. Rosalind wasn't quite sure what she had expected, but it wasn't to be blamed for Simon's predicament. Simon accused her of being obsessed with Jamie, of deliberately disappearing just when he needed her.

'If you'd been here, none of this would have happened,' he told her angrily, ordering her back to London at once, so that they could show a united front to the press pack waiting outside his door.

'I can't come back,' said Rosalind. 'There's still someone out there who wants to harm Jamie.'

'For God's sake, Rosalind, my career's on the line here!'

'So is Jamie's safety,' she retorted.

'You're my fiancée,' Simon reminded her coldly. 'Your place is with me. I need you here, not hidden away in some godforsaken hole in Yorkshire.'

Rosalind looked out at the godforsaken hole, clean and green and tranquil in the spring sunshine. 'You can look after yourself,' she said. 'Jamie can't.'

'We had an agreement,' he said, controlling his frustration with difficulty. 'You said we'd make a good team. With you by my side I could even be in with a chance for a top job. You can't throw it all away just because of one little indiscretion!'

'It wasn't my indiscretion,' Rosalind pointed out.

'If you hadn't been so damned frigid, I wouldn't have had to be indiscreet!' he snarled. 'At least Lydia was some fun. And don't tell me you haven't been sleeping with that brother of Emma's while you've been away. Very convenient for you, pretending to be married! The only difference between us is that you haven't been found out!'

'Would you mind, Simon, if I had been sleeping with him?' asked Rosalind.

'Of course not!' Obviously regretting losing his temper, Simon switched to a wheedling tone. 'We don't have that kind of relationship, do we? You can do whatever you like. Wasn't that part of our agreement? As long as you're discreet, I won't interfere with you. I'll send a car up to fetch you tonight, and we can work out some story when you get back. Once the papers see that you're standing by me, they'll lose interest.'

It took some time for Rosalind to convince Simon that she had no intention of returning to London yet. When she'd succeeded, he launched into a venomous tirade that made her wonder how she could ever have considered marrying him, and her hands were shaking by the time she put down the phone.

'Rosalind, are you all right?' Michael came into the kitchen where she was washing dishes after dinner that night.

The concern in his voice made Rosalind's eyes sting with tears, but her humiliation was too raw for her to admit it to anyone, least of all to him. She bent her head over the washing up bowl and pretended to concentrate on scouring a saucepan. 'I'm fine. Why shouldn't I be?'

'I thought you looked upset about something,' he said, watching her too closely for comfort. 'You've been very quiet all evening.'

'I've got a bit of a headache, that's all. I think I'll have a bath and go to bed.'

'Go now,' said Michael gruffly. 'I'll finish these.'

Rosalind lay in the bath and let the tears trickle down her cheeks at last. Simon had hurt her more than she would have believed possible. It wasn't his affair, it was the dislike in his voice when she had refused to bring Jamie out of hiding. Unconsciously echoing the opinion of Maud's neighbours, he had accused her of being cold and hard and selfish.

It had been easy enough to dismiss the neighbours, who had been going on no more than a few snippets in the gossip columns, but how she could ignore what Simon thought? Rosalind had thought that he liked her and respected her, but apparently he didn't. It seemed that he didn't like her any more than anyone else. Perhaps there wasn't anything about her *to* like.

Lonely, hurt and humiliated, Rosalind turned her cheek into the cool enamel and wept.

'Rosalind!' It was Michael, knocking on the bathroom door.

'Go away!' she gulped, not wanting him to see her crying, but none of Maud's doors had locks on them, and Michael came in anyway.

'I said, go away!' Rosalind turned her face away.

'Emma's just rung,' he said, apparently oblivious to her nakedness. 'She wanted to know if you were OK.' He paused, looking down at her averted face. 'She told me about Simon. Why didn't you tell me?'

Rosalind opened her mouth to inform him that it was none of his business, but found herself bursting into noisy tears instead. Appalled at herself, she struggled up and buried her face in her hands.

'Come on.' Michael put a hard hand beneath her elbow and helped her out of the bath, wrapping her in the towel like a child and sitting down with her in his lap. Rosalind gave in and buried her face in his throat, sobbing out her pain and humiliation while Michael held her close and made soothing noises.

'How did you find out?' he asked at last.

'I saw the papers when I went to get the milk,' she gulped. 'I rang Simon from the call box.'

'What did he say?'

'He said it was all my fault for being so uptight and obsessed with Jamie.' She couldn't seem to stop crying, and Michael tightened his arms and rocked her gently.

'I'm so sorry, Rosalind.'

'I'm not crying for Simon,' she wept. 'I just feel so stupid. I thought he liked me, but he doesn't. He thinks I'm boring and frigid, and he said at least Lydia was *fun*!' The words were tumbling from her, punctuated by hiccuping sobs. 'He said he didn't think I'd care. He accused me of having an affair with you, he said we were bound to be sleeping together.'

'We nearly did,' Michael reminded her.

'I wish we had!' she said, muffled against his throat. 'You must think me such a fool, banging on about loyalty and not sleeping with you because of that stupid agreement, and all the time Simon couldn't care less!'

'I don't think you're a fool at all, Rosalind. I think you deserve better than him.'

Her sobs had subsided enough for her to notice how comforting it was to lean into him and feel his arms around her. He was still rocking her like a baby, murmuring soft shushing noises, his cheek resting on her hair. Slowly, Rosalind let her distress seep away as she breathed in the warm, male scent of his skin.

'Simon wants me to go back,' she muttered after a while. 'He says if I don't go, I'll ruin his career.'

Michael stilled. 'Are you going?'

'What do you think I should do?'

'I think you should stay here until you know it's safe to take Jamie home,' he said firmly. 'Simon has ruined his own career. If he had made an effort to contact you himself, to warn you, if he had even apologised when you rang him, it might be different, but all he's done is try and put the blame on you. You can't marry a man like that. I think you should let him sort his own mess out.'

Rosalind sat back a little on his knee and looked at him, longing to be persuaded. Her eyes were swollen, her nose red, the perfect skin blotched. 'Do you really think so?'

'I know so,' said Michael, smoothing back her hair. 'And I know something else, too. You're not frigid, Rosalind.'

Gently, he pulled her head towards him so that he could kiss her on her trembling mouth. It began as a tender, reassuring kiss, but somewhere in the middle of it something changed, and the old excitement flickered into life. Without thinking, Rosalind put her arms round Michael's neck and sank into him, misery forgotten as she gave back kiss for kiss—long, deep kisses that grew in urgency as the flicker became a flame and the flame a fire.

'You see,' said Michael breathlessly after a while. 'You're not frigid at all, are you?'

Rosalind looked at him with frank, tear-drenched green eyes. 'Not with you,' she said.

He smiled. 'Come on,' he said, tipping her off his lap and taking a firm hold of her hand as he stood up. 'I think it's time we gave that chemistry a chance!'

Clutching at her towel, Rosalind allowed herself to be pulled along to the bedroom, but once inside the door, she warded him off with her hands. 'Michael, what about Kathy?'

'Ah, Kathy...' Michael had the grace to look a little embarrassed. He sat down on the bed and pulled off his shoes and socks. 'I'm afraid I misled you a bit about Kathy. We were together for a while, but she went back home to the States before Christmas. She's a good friend, but no more than that.'

'Really?'

Michael looked at Rosalind, who was still lurking by the door, holding her towel together with both her hands. 'Yes, really,' he said as he stood up and came towards her, his eyes alight with laughter. 'So you see, there's really no reason for us not to give in to the chemistry!'

'Oh.' Still she hung back, absurdly nervous, retreating before Michael until her back was against the door.

'What is it now?' he teased, and she blushed.

'I don't want you to make love to me just because you feel sorry for me,' she muttered.

'If I feel sorry for anyone, it's me, for having to wait this long for you,' Michael pretended to grumble as he closed the gap between them and took her face between his palms. Then the laughter faded from his face. 'This is what we both wanted four days ago, Rosalind,' he said. 'And it's what we both want now.' His hands dropped from her face to draw her closer, so that he could nuzzle the side of her neck and drop slow, seductive kisses along her bare shoulder. 'Isn't it?'

Quivering under the enticing onslaught of his lips, Rosalind could only nod.

'Tonight, there's just the two of us,' whispered Michael.

'And the chemistry,' she sighed, letting out a long breath of release as she gave in to temptation at last and wound her arms around his neck. His lips were still searing up her throat, so she kissed his ear, his cheek, blizzarding her way along his jaw until she found his mouth at last for a kiss that was deep and rich with promise.

Michael's fingers were loosening her towel. It fell in a soft heap behind her, and Rosalind smiled at the expression on his face as his eyes travelled over her naked body, still damp and gleaming in parts. 'Rosalind...' he said, and the hoarseness in his voice sent sweet expectancy bubbling along her veins. Eyes dark with need, she watched as he tugged off his shirt and jumper together in one impatient movement and flung them aside.

There was nothing now to stop her spreading her hands over his bare chest. Rosalind moved closer. The first feel of his flesh beneath her fingers was so exciting that she drew a sharp intake of breath, hardly able to believe that at last—at last!—she could savour the sleek warmth of his skin and the leashed power of his muscles. Pressing her mouth to his bare shoulder, she felt Michael tense in response, and the next moment he had swept her up and was carrying her over to the bed, where he laid her down and stripped off the rest of his clothes.

They lay facing each other, the knowledge of what was to come beating through them, impatience fading with the realisation that they had all night to rediscover each other. Almost wonderingly, Michael traced the outline of Rosalind's mouth with his fingers before letting them drift down to the hollow at the base of her throat.

'Do you know how often I've thought about this, Rosalind?' he murmured, as he pressed a kiss to it and let his hand continue its devastating exploration. 'Every night we've spent in this damned bed, I've lain here and thought about how close you were.'

'I know.' Rosalind was awash with sheer pleasure. 'I know. It was the same for me. All I wanted was to roll over and touch you like this,' she whispered, her hands moving hungrily over him. His body was lean and hard, all supple strength, and she ran her hands insistently over him, savouring the feel of muscles that were as hard as steel yet flexed so responsively beneath her fingers.

'Did you think about this?' Michael's fingers gentled over her skin, remembering the sweet curves and hollows of her body.

'Yes,' she breathed.

'And this?' Searing, scorching, his hands moved on, stroking, circling, teasing, drawing patterns of desire on her skin, and his lips followed, touching her, tasting her, arousing her until she could hardly breathe.

She was on fire. 'Yes, yes!' Gasping his name, arching beneath that wickedly enticing touch, Rosalind lost track of time. She was swirling helplessly along in a torrent of sensation so intense it scared her, where there was only the heart-stopping feel of flesh on flesh, the delicious roughness of male skin against hers. Only the hard demand of his hands and the insistent, intoxicating, exploration of his lips. Only the pounding of desire and the hunger that grew moment by moment, sweeping them up together in a great, surging wave.

Inexorable, irresistible, it bore them on and on beyond imagination until it left them clinging desperately to each other, poised dizzyingly above an abyss, and Rosalind cried out again and again as it came crashing down with them at last in a wild, turbulent rush of release.

CHAPTER NINE

'MICHAEL?' Much, much later, Rosalind stirred. She was nestled into his side, her head on his shoulder, his arm close and reassuring around her. It felt so right to be there, she thought, smoothing her hand over his chest. It was like coming home. How long had it been since she had felt this contented, relaxed and replete and rippling with delight?

Not for five years. Not since the last time Michael had made love to her.

'Michael?' she said again.

'Mmm?'

'Did you mean what you said about not being in a relationship with Kathy any more?'

Michael opened one eye and squinted down at her. 'Yes.'

'Why did you pretend you were still in love with her?'

'Oh, I don't know. It seemed like a good idea at the time. You'd been talking about your engagement to Simon, and I suppose I was still pretty raw about the way things ended five years ago. I felt I needed to prove to you that someone wanted me, even if you didn't.' He grimaced up at the ceiling. 'Childish, I know. I'd forgotten what I'd told you about Kathy until you brought her up again after the party, and then it seemed easier to let it go. I had other things on my mind.' Michael shifted so that he could lean up on one arm and smile down into Rosalind's face as his hand slid lingeringly over her hip. 'Like how I was going to keep my hands off you.'

Rosalind stretched luxuriously beneath his touch. 'I'm sorry about that night,' she said.

'Don't be,' said Michael. 'You did the right thing.'

'It didn't feel very right,' she confessed. 'It seems such a waste of time. We could have been spending every night like this.'

'We've still got some nights to come,' he reminded her, and Rosalind lifted her hands to his shoulders, smoothing them almost thoughtfully over the powerful muscles.

'When will you have to go back?'

His smile faded slightly. 'I've got another couple of weeks.'

'Two weeks,' echoed Rosalind, hoping that the dismay didn't show in her face. What had she expected, that this would last for ever? She mustered a smile. 'The night of the party you said we should just accept the chemistry and make the most of the time we had together.'

'I still think that,' said Michael, his hand moving tantalisingly downwards once more, making it difficult for her to think. 'Neither of us has any expectations beyond that,' he reassured her. 'I think we should just enjoy the next two weeks and not waste time thinking about the future.' He bent to kiss her shoulder. 'What do you think?'

His lips were warm, his hands persuasive. Rosalind linked her arms behind his neck and closed her mind to the sudden cold perception of how bleak life would be when the two weeks were over. 'Well…' She pretended to deliberate, pulling his head down to murmur against his mouth. 'I suppose it *would* be a shame to give up on the chemistry. It does seem to be working well, doesn't it?'

'It does,' smiled Michael as he lowered his body onto hers. 'It does indeed!'

'I think you and Jamie should come with us to York,' said Maud. 'Michael's coming to the solicitor with me, but we won't be that long. You haven't been anywhere or done anything since you arrived,' she went on. 'You need a break.'

Rosalind didn't think that she did. She was happy in Askerby. She wanted time to stand still so that she could stay just where she was, where Jamie was safe and happy, where the days were filled with laughter and the nights with delight. It had been a week since she and Michael had made love for the first time, and every night since had been better than the last as they rediscovered each other's body. Why would she need a break from that?

But Maud was insistent, and Jamie instantly alert to the possibility of a treat. Rosalind smiled and allowed herself to be persuaded. An uneasy voice at the back of her mind was counting down the days until Michael had to go back to the Middle East. Right now, she didn't really care where she was as long as he was there too.

Rosalind sat in the back of the car with Jamie, while Maud occupied the front seat, directing Michael with magnificent gestures and a complete lack of consideration for anyone else on the road. Michael nodded, but managed to find a car park close to the city centre by completely ignoring her instructions.

Rosalind hardly heard Maud's voice. Her eyes were on the back of Michael's head, her mind on the night before. They had made love so slow, so sure, so intoxicatingly sweet that she had cried. She looked at his neck above his collar. She knew just what it felt like to kiss the side of his throat below his ear, to tickle his lobe with her tongue and taste his skin, and desire swamped her without warning.

She wanted to lean forward, to wind her arms around his neck and whisper in his ear. She wanted to tell him to pull over, to stop the car. She wanted him to turn in his seat so that she could kiss him properly. She wanted him to take her back to Askerby and lead her up to the bedroom. She wanted him to lay her down on the bed and make love to her all over again.

'Rosalind?'

Rosalind came to with a start and realised that she had been staring at an empty seat. One eyebrow raised enquiringly, Michael was holding her door open, while Maud and Jamie waited with identically puzzled expressions.

'Oh, sorry…' Rosalind climbed out, suddenly self-conscious. 'I was dreaming,' she explained awkwardly.

Jamie tucked his hand in hers. 'Was it a nice dream?'

Instinctively, she glanced at Michael. He was watching her, grey eyes alight with amusement, and her heart turned over. She was sure that he knew exactly what she had been thinking about. 'Yes,' she said to Jamie, an answering smile trembling on her lips, 'it was.'

Michael locked the car and put his arm around her waist as they followed Maud and Jamie towards the city walls. 'Are you going to tell me about it?' he murmured with a squeeze, and Rosalind smiled.

'Later,' she promised.

The solicitor's office was tucked away down a tiny alleyway. If Maud hadn't known where she was going, they might never have found it. Michael glanced at

Rosalind as they paused in front of the fine Georgian door. 'I don't know how long we'll be. Not very long. Do you want to wait?'

She shook her head. 'No, we'll go and have a wander around.'

'Are you sure you'll be all right?'

'Yes,' said Rosalind, and knew that she would be. In London, the crowded streets had terrified her. She had scuttled between her door and the limousine, constantly aware that one of those passing might be the one who was watching and waiting for an opportunity to snatch Jamie from her. But no one so much as glanced at them as they walked in through the massive city gates. The centre was busy, but the crowds were good-humoured, strolling along in the sunshine, enjoying the absence of cars, and Rosalind and Jamie merged effortlessly into them.

She couldn't remember the last time she had dawdled like this, drifting with the flow, looking in shop windows without any urge to go inside and spend. There seemed to be street performers at every corner. Music from classical quartets faded into pan pipes, which gave way in their turn to banjos and then opera. They stopped for a while to watch two jugglers, tossing fiery torches in the air, and Jamie's eyes were as big as saucers.

When they found their way back to the solicitor's office, Michael was waiting for them outside the door. Spotting him first, Jamie ran towards him to be swung up in the air, and Rosalind was laughing at his enthusiasm as she came up more slowly. Then her laughter faded as she caught sight of the peculiar expression on Michael's face.

'What's the matter?'

'Nothing,' he said. 'I was just watching you come

towards me through the crowd and thinking how you stood out.'

Puzzled, Rosalind glanced down at her sweatshirt and jeans. 'How can I stand out in this?' she asked.

'I don't know,' said Michael. 'You just do.'

A blush crept up her cheeks. 'What have you done with Maud?' she said, trying to pretend that she wasn't ridiculously pleased by such an innocuous compliment.

'Her solicitor is taking her out to lunch. I said we'd meet her back here in a couple of hours.' He looked down at Jamie, still swinging on his hand. 'What shall we do? Shall we have a picnic?'

'And ice cream?'

Michael laughed. 'And ice cream!'

Together, they walked through the gardens around the ruined abbey, Jamie skipping and jumping between them as he hung on their hands. The grass was scattered with people making the most of the sunshine, but they managed to find a space for themselves where they could admire the peacocks strutting around, trailing their magnificent tails and disdainfully ignoring attempts to call them over.

Having eaten his sandwich in record time, Jamie was rewarded with an ice cream which he ate with a beatific expression and the maximum of mess. Rosalind shook her head, but smiled as she wiped the worst of it off and let him run off to chase the pigeons.

'He's having a good time,' Michael commented lazily, lying back with his hands under his head.

'Yes.' Rosalind clasped her hands around her knees, a wistful expression in her eyes as they rested on her little brother. 'I never did anything like this when I was a child,' she confessed. 'Sometimes my father would take me with him to the Caribbean. It's a lovely place, of course, but because of security I was never allowed outside the grounds, and he spent most of his time on the phone working. There was a pool, but there was a pool in the London house as well, so I might as well have stayed at home.' She sighed. 'I would much rather he'd bought me an ice cream in the park occasionally.'

There was a pause. Michael watched Jamie too. He was running around in circles, arms outspread, small face alight. 'You're doing the right thing, making sure Jamie doesn't have such a sheltered childhood,' he said after a while.

'I'm only doing it because of you.' Rosalind turned to look down at him, lounging, relaxed and self-contained as ever, beside her, and the breath leaked out of her lungs. He was very distinct, at once intensely familiar and yet oddly a stranger. She felt as if she had never seen the texture of his skin before, never noticed the darkness of his lashes. Every crease around his eyes stood out with unsettling clarity, and she was suddenly, preternaturally conscious of the smell of the grass, of the children's shouts ringing through the warm spring air, of the feel of denim against her skin.

With an effort she made herself look away. 'You've made it easy for us to be normal,' she said unevenly. 'I would never have considered taking him for a picnic in the park before. I was too worried about security, like my father, but I can see now that he needs to get out and run around like all the other little boys. I'll make much more of an effort with him when we get home.'

When we get home. The words hung between them, and there was a sudden dismayed silence, as if a crevasse had opened up beneath their feet.

Michael sat up, hunching his shoulders forward to rest his arms on his knees. 'Have you thought about what you're going to do if you haven't heard from the police before I go?'

His voice was very steady, and Rosalind made an effort to sound as unconcerned by the prospect of his leaving. 'I'll have to go back some time,' she said, trying to imagine what it would be like to be in London again, able to have whatever she wanted, whenever she wanted. Except the one thing she couldn't have.

Michael.

The gardens seemed to tilt around her, and instinctively Rosalind put out her hands to steady herself on the grass as the truth hit her. She loved him.

She loved him. She *loved* him.

There was a hollow ache inside her, an almost despairing sense that her life would never be the same now that she had fallen so utterly, so irrevocably, in love. After all these years of telling herself that she didn't need love, that she would settle for less rather than risk the hurt of not being loved in return, she had to fall in love with Michael, the one man she couldn't have.

Rosalind looked at him and felt giddy with the longing to say it, just once: *I love you.* It would be so easy to say. She could shout it out loud, so everyone in the gardens would hear. The impulse was so strong that the words hovered on her lips, but she bit them back. It wouldn't be fair to Michael. He had offered her his love once, and she had thrown it away. She couldn't ask for it back now. He had made it plain that he had a life of his own, one that she could have no part in.

Neither of us has any expectations, he had said. *I think we should just enjoy the next two weeks and not waste time thinking about the future.*

Those two weeks had shortened to one, and if they were going to make the most of that, she mustn't let him guess how she felt. She mustn't spoil the time they had left. Rosalind drew a deep, steadying breath. 'Even if they haven't found the stalker, I'll be able to cope with it better now.' She let herself look at him. 'I haven't thanked you properly for everything you've done for us, Michael,' she said. 'I don't know what Jamie and I would have done without you.'

'You don't need to thank me, Rosalind,' he said, turning his head to look deep into her eyes. 'I've enjoyed being with Jamie.' He paused. 'And with you,' he added softly, tucking a stray hair behind her ear.

Rosalind's heart was drumming, her cheek burning where his fingers had grazed her skin. She was held by his eyes, pinioned by the light in them that told her that she could whisper that she loved him and he would believe her and forgive her for the way she had hurt him before.

'There's something I want to tell you,' said Michael, as if suddenly making up his mind about something.

'What is it?' she said breathlessly.

'I've been thinking about the things you said the night of the party, about only being liked for your money or your appearance,' he said carefully. 'You said you didn't think you were a very likeable person. I just want to tell you that you are. I like you. I like you a lot.'

Rosalind's eyes stung with tears. It wasn't quite what she wanted to hear, but it was more than she had hoped, and more than she deserved. 'Do you?' she whispered.

Michael nodded. 'I used not to. You were right when you said that I fell in love with your body before.' He glanced at her. 'You were so beautiful, Rosalind. I don't think you realise what an effect you had on me. I'd heard so much about you from Emma. I thought you sounded a bad influence on her, and when I met you it seemed to me that you were just as vain and superficial as I'd expected. I was ready to disapprove of you and instead I found myself in thrall to you.'

He paused to see if Rosalind was looking. 'I've always hated standing in queues,' he said apologetically. 'The last thing I wanted was to get involved with you, but I couldn't help myself. I hated what I saw as my own weakness, and I resented you for making me feel that way.'

Rosalind plucked at some grass. 'Why did you ask me to marry you if that's how you felt?'

'I didn't mean to. I took myself by surprise as much as you,' Michael recalled with a rueful smile. 'I came to tell you that I'd got a job overseas. I thought it would be the perfect opportunity to end an affair that we both knew couldn't last, but then you turned and ran your fingers through your hair, and you smiled at me, and suddenly the thought of never seeing you again was unendurable.'

She spread her hands on the grass on either side of her, remembering how he had grabbed her arm and swung her round to face him. 'Marry me,' he had demanded urgently. 'Come with me.' Thrown off balance, she had laughed in his face. How could she have known that he would be the only man she would ever love?

'I'm sorry I hurt you, Michael,' she said in a low voice. She had wanted to say those words for a long time now, since she had seen his face as he turned and walked out of the room and out of her life. 'I didn't want things to end that way.'

They were both silent, remembering the bitter things they had said to each other. 'Perhaps that's the only way it could have ended,' said Michael after a moment.

'I don't know,' sighed Rosalind, leaning back on her

hands, looking at the sunlit ruins of the abbey but seeing the past. 'I could have been kinder, if nothing else. You caught me off balance. I was so used to thinking of you as disapproving of me and I was shaken when I realised that you were serious. Then I got angry,' she remembered sadly, thinking how different things were now. 'It seemed as if you'd asked me to marry you against your will, and my pride was hurt, and the next thing I knew I'd lost my temper.'

Michael lifted his shoulders, as if shrugging off the past. 'It doesn't matter now. You were right to turn me down. I lost my head and asked you to marry me without thinking what it would mean. God knows what I'd have done with a wife like you out in the middle of the desert! It would have been a disaster.'

'Yes.' Rosalind winced inwardly. Michael was just confirming what she had always known, but it had never hurt the way it did now that she knew how much she loved him. 'Yes, it would never have worked, but...' Her voice trailed off.

'But what?' he prompted.

'But I didn't know I'd miss you so much when you were gone,' she admitted. 'I wished I hadn't said those awful things to you. I wished I'd thanked you for the good times we'd had.' She turned her head to look into his alert grey eyes. 'But most of all I wished we'd had a chance to say goodbye properly.'

'It's a little late,' said Michael, 'but perhaps this is it. We've both made mistakes, Rosalind. We can't change them by changing the past, but we've been given a chance to change the ending.' He held out his hand. 'This time, let's enjoy the time we've got together and say goodbye without regrets.'

Rosalind looked at his hand, then laid her own in it,

twining her fingers with his. Her heart ached at the thought of saying goodbye to him, but it was obvious that Michael had no intention of repeating the mistakes of the past. *It would have been a disaster,* he had said. It probably still would.

She swallowed a painful lump in her throat. 'Yes, let's do that,' she said, and his hand tightened around hers to pull her towards him for a kiss that sealed the promise.

'You'll be all right, Rosalind,' said Michael with an edge of urgency as he let her go. 'Don't listen to what other people say. There's plenty to like about you.'

She managed a wavering smile. 'Thank you.'

'Well?' Michael's own smile was rather twisted. 'Aren't you going to tell me whether you like me?'

'Oh, yes,' she breathed, her eyes shimmering with tears. 'Oh, yes, I do!' Leaning into him, she kissed him again. She had meant it to be a brief, tender kiss, but their lips caught and clung, and then Michael was pushing her back down onto the grass and honeyed enchantment was flooding through her.

'Isn't it time you told me what you were dreaming about in the car?' he murmured unsteadily against her mouth at last, and Rosalind wound her arms tighter around his neck to pull him closer once more. She only had a week left with Michael and she was going to make the most of it.

'I thought I just did.'

It was Jamie who recalled them to a sense of their surroundings, standing over them and demanding to know whether they were practising again. 'Practising?' Rosalind sat up, blushing and tidying her hair. Then she remembered how Michael had kissed her at Maud's gate on the day they arrived in Askerby, and she laughed. 'Yes, Jamie, that's just what we were doing!'

'What for?'

Her eyes met Michael's and anticipation shivered down her spine. 'For tonight.'

The phone was ringing as Maud opened the door when they got back to Askerby, but it stopped just as she was about to pick up the receiver. 'If they want to talk to me that badly, they can ring again,' she said, unimpressed by the advantages of an answer-machine that Rosalind had outlined to her.

Maud was right. The phone rang again later that evening, just as Rosalind was coming downstairs after putting a thoroughly over-excited Jamie to bed. 'I'll get it,' she called, running lightly down the last two steps into the hall.

'Roz, where have you *been*?' Emma's excited voice came down the line as she answered. 'I've been trying to ring you all day!'

'We've been to York—' Rosalind broke off. 'Why, what's happened?'

'It's wonderful news! The police came round to say that they've arrested Sandra Danelli on charges of harassment.'

'Sandra?' Rosalind couldn't believe it. 'There must be some mistake. Sandra's a friend of the family. I've known her for years…it can't be her!'

'I'm afraid it is,' said Emma. 'Apparently she's admitted everything, so you don't need to worry any more. You can come home as soon as you want!'

Rosalind put down the receiver slowly when Emma had finished. She stood in the cold hall, looking down at the telephone. Emma had obviously been puzzled by her less than enthusiastic reception of the news, but then

Emma wasn't to know that Rosalind didn't want to go home, and that now she had no excuse to stay.

Michael came out of the kitchen. 'Who was that?' he asked idly, and then stopped as he saw Rosalind's expression.

'Emma,' she said.

'They've found your stalker.' The words came out flatly, not even a question.

'Yes.'

There was a pause. 'You must be very relieved.'

'Yes,' said Rosalind. She didn't *sound* very relieved, she realised. She sounded desperate. 'Yes, yes, I am,' she tried again.

'Did Emma tell you who it was?'

She nodded. 'I still can't believe it. Sandra's a family friend—or so I thought. She told the police that she was my father's mistress for several years. I suppose that explains why she was always around, but disappeared after his marriage to Natasha.' Rosalind shook her head at her own naivety. 'I had no idea. I knew my father had girlfriends, of course, but I didn't think any of them were special. I don't think *he* thought so either, until he met Natasha. Apparently it sent Sandra over the edge. She'd been pretending to herself that Daddy would marry her, and by that time it was too late for her to have the children she wanted.'

Rosalind sighed at the waste of it. 'I gather she began to feel very bitter about the fact that my father had two children and she didn't have any, and it seems to have grown into an obsession after his death.'

'How did the police find out that it was her?' asked Michael. They were talking like strangers, neither of them ready to accept what the arrest would mean to them.

'Apparently she was very frustrated when we disappeared with you.' Rosalind knew she ought to sound as if she cared, but the terrible fear of being watched the whole time seemed to belong to a different life altogether. It was as if she had read about it in a book. 'I'm not really sure what happened, but she seems to have taken one risk too many to find out where we'd gone and that roused suspicion.'

'What will happen to her now?'

She lifted her hands in a helpless gesture. 'I suppose it depends whether I press charges or not. I hated it when I was scared and she seemed to have taken over my life, but now I just think she must be so sad…' She trailed off, then recollected herself. 'I'll have to talk to the police.'

Michael hesitated. 'So there's nothing to stop you going back to London straight away?'

Rosalind felt as if she was teetering on the brink of a precipice. 'No.'

She waited for him to suggest that she stay a while longer, at least until he had to leave, but he didn't.

'We'll tell Maud that the phone call was from a member of your family who's had an accident,' he said. His jaw was rigid, but his voice was very even. 'You can say that you need to go tomorrow.'

'You don't think I should tell Maud the truth?' said Rosalind, when she could master the disappointment in her voice. 'It doesn't seem right to carry on deceiving her now that there's no need.'

'I think it's better if I tell her when you've gone,' he said. 'She'll be upset, and it would be kinder not to ask her to put on a brave face in front of Jamie when you say goodbye.'

'All right,' Rosalind agreed in a dull voice.

Michael set his jaw and ploughed on. 'I'll take you to York. It'll be easiest if you get a train from there to London. You'll be home in two hours.'

'Fine.'

So that was it. She was to be put on the first train home, Rosalind thought, torn between misery and bitterness. Dimly, she was aware that it might be easier that way, rather than prolonging the agony, but it didn't make any difference to the overpowering sense of hurt.

Maud was very concerned to hear about Rosalind's grandmother's fall. 'My dear, you'll be sick of looking after old ladies!' she exclaimed. 'I do wish you didn't have to go, but I mustn't be selfish. It's been such a comfort to me the way you've taken over all the housework and got the house back under control, as I'm sure it will be to your grandmother. Where does she live?'

'London,' lied Rosalind.

'Well, it won't be much fun for Jamie there,' said Maud, with all the assurance of someone who hadn't visited the capital for forty years. 'Why doesn't Michael keep him here?'

'I'm not sure how long I'll have to stay,' Rosalind said after a tiny moment. 'Michael may have to go back without us.'

'Are you *sure* you wouldn't like him to go with you?' Maud offered, although it had already been agreed that Michael would stay with her.

No, Rosalind wanted to shout, I'm not sure! But all she could do was smile a brief, brittle smile and say that she would be fine.

If only she had had the courage to tell him she loved him in the gardens, she thought as she lay in bed later that evening and waited for Michael to come back from the bathroom. Now it was too late. If he had loved her, he would have begged her not to go, or at least suggested that she stay a little bit longer, but he hadn't. 'I'll take you to York.' That was all he had said.

The next moment, the breath leaked out of her body as Michael came in. He hesitated by the door, then crossed over to sit on the edge of the bed, close to her but not close enough to touch.

'This will be our last chance to talk,' he said, sounding strained. 'There won't be any time in the morning.'

'No,' Rosalind agreed, pulling herself up against the pillows. She wasn't sure that she wanted to talk. She wanted him to make love to her one last time, without wasting the few hours they had left on stilted conversation.

'Well, we had a bad start.' It sounded as if Michael was only keeping his voice light with an effort. 'But it's been good, hasn't it?'

'Yes,' she said, 'it has.'

'It's better to end it this way,' he made himself go on. 'It's what we agreed.'

'I know.' Rosalind's throat was tight. She had to end this before she cried. 'Michael?'

He turned and looked into her face, a long look that squeezed her heart. 'Yes?'

Rosalind swallowed. Reaching out, she laid her hand against his flank. His flesh was warm and firm and it shivered in instinctive response. 'We've still got tonight,' she reminded him. 'We've said all there is to be said. Let's not say goodbye until tomorrow.'

She watched as he undressed, gazing longingly at the lean planes of his body, storing up memories of its compact grace and masculine hardness. Then she pulled back the sheet and shifted over the bed so that he could slide in beside her, savouring the moment of breathless anticipation before flesh met flesh.

They made love that night with an edge of desperation. Rosalind abandoned herself to the feel of his hands and his lips, to the glorious, heart-stopping feel of his body possessing hers. She ran her fingers over him urgently, digging them into his flesh, frantic to lose herself in the last mind-shattering explosion of ecstasy.

Afterwards, they held each other silently until they slept. In the early morning, they made love one last time. Their loving was so indescribably sweet, so terrifying in its intensity, that they cried out together, but still there were no words. They both knew that there was nothing left to say.

CHAPTER TEN

'THE next train on Platform 3 will be the 10:05 to London King's Cross.'

Rosalind stared along the long, curved platform, willing the train to arrive. She had been dreading this moment all morning, and now all she wanted was to get it over with before she broke down and begged Michael to let her stay.

They had hardly said anything to each other since she had finished packing the few things she was taking with her. Sitting on the edge of the bed, she had looked down at the wedding band on her hand for a moment before tugging it slowly off her finger. It had been like pulling away part of herself, and pain had twisted in her heart. She'd swallowed.

'You'd better have your mother's ring back,' she said as she held it out to Michael. 'We don't need it any more.'

'No,' said Michael, 'I suppose we don't.'

Rosalind tried to smile. 'I hope that next time you use it, it will be for real.'

'Yes.' His voice sounded flat, and his mouth was slightly twisted as he looked down at the ring he held in his hand, then, in an abrupt movement, he shoved it in his pocket, as if pushing away an unpleasant thought and turned for the door. 'If you're ready, we'd better go.'

It was agony saying goodbye to Maud. Rosalind's throat was so tight with the effort of not crying that she could hardly speak. All she could do was mutter an inadequate goodbye and hug Maud hard. Maud herself seemed to be finding it nearly as difficult as Rosalind was. She didn't cry either, but her lips were clamped firmly together to stop them wobbling as she hugged first Jamie and then Rosalind.

'I'll miss you,' she managed, and Rosalind nodded. For Maud, as for her, a golden time had come to a sudden end, and there was nothing either of them could do about it.

'We'll miss you too.'

There was a cold, leaden stone inside her, weighing her down, making it hard to move. Rosalind walked stiffly down the path to where Michael was waiting in the car. Everything was an immense physical effort: opening the gate, pulling the car door closed, lifting a hand to wave to Maud, forcing her lips apart in a ghastly smile. As Michael turned the car around and pointed it back in the direction of York, she felt as if she were being torn away, like a limpet from a rock.

They had hardly got into third gear before Laura Osborne waved them down outside the village shop. 'I'm so glad I caught you,' she said, smiling at both of them through the window that Michael had wound down. 'I know it's short notice, but I wondered if you and Maud would come round to dinner tomorrow night?'

'I'm afraid we're just on our way to the station,' said Michael after a tiny pause. 'Rosalind and Jamie have got to go down to London today.'

'Oh, what a pity!' Laura even looked as if she meant it. 'You're not going as well, Michael?'

'No.'

'Well, perhaps you and Maud could come?'

'I'll mention it to her,' Michael said. 'I'm sure she'd like to.'

'Good.' Laura stepped back from the window. 'Well, I'd better not hold you up. I'm sorry you won't be able to make it, Rosalind. Tom will miss Jamie. When will you be back?'

Rosalind drew an unsteady breath as she faced the truth. 'I'm not coming back,' she said.

They drove out of the village in silence. Rosalind told herself that she had to get used to the idea of Michael doing things without her. This was the end. He had his life and she had hers. She sat looking straight ahead, torturing herself with memories of how different things had been only yesterday, when they had driven along exactly the same route. Then she had been distracted, happy, tingling still with memories of the night before and brimming with anticipation of the night to come. Now the future yawned bleakly ahead of her. She was at the start of a tangent, taking her away from Michael, further and further every day, and there was nothing she could do but pretend that it was what she wanted.

Michael found a parking space at the station, and carried Jamie's small case as they made their way to the ticket office. Rosalind had a handbag and what she stood up in: jeans and a plain white shirt, with a cotton jumper slung round her shoulders. She had left everything else that Emma had bought her in Askerby. Michael had promised to get rid of them for her.

There had been a moment when Rosalind had almost been tempted to take it all with her, if only because it would remind her of when she had been so happy, but in the end she decided to leave it. It was a symbolic gesture, a way of casting her disguise aside, just as recharging her mobile phone was a first step to resuming her real life. There was no reason to pretend that she wasn't Rosalind Leigh any more, no reason not to buy a first-class ticket, no reason not to say goodbye.

There was a stir along the platform now, as the London train drew in and slid to a halt with a great hissing of brakes. Immediately small knots of passengers converged on every door, then had to stand back and wait while others got off.

Michael set his jaw. 'Here you go, Jamie,' he said with false cheer. 'What about getting in this carriage?'

A little over-awed by the size and noise of the train now that it was here, Jamie nodded but kept tight hold of Rosalind's hand. Michael swung the case easily in through the door. 'I'd better not get on,' he said, 'but it's not heavy. You should be able to manage it.'

'Of course,' said Rosalind. She felt as if she were made of fine porcelain with a crack running through her, fearing the final touch that would shatter her into a thousand pieces. Her voice was high and strained with the effort of keeping herself together. 'Jamie, say goodbye to Michael.'

It was the first time Jamie had realised that Michael would not be going with them. His bottom lip trembled. 'Want Michael to come!'

'I can't come, Jamie.' Michael scooped him up and hugged him hard. 'Be a good boy, and look after Rosalind for me,' he said. 'She's not used to public transport, and she'll need you to show her what to do.'

Setting Jamie down, he turned to Rosalind, who was watching him with anguished green eyes, and there was a terrible, despairing silence when it seemed that they could do nothing but look at each other.

This was the last time she would see him, Rosalind realised in something like panic. She couldn't go without thanking him, without telling him what he had meant to her. 'Michael,' she began, then stopped, unable to go on. How could she find the right words when their last seconds together were ticking away and any moment now the train would leave? 'Michael, I—'

Her voice wavered treacherously, and Michael took her in his arms. 'You don't need to say anything,' he said, and kissed her, one last, long kiss that said more than words ever could. 'Goodbye, Rosalind,' he said softly when he lifted his head, and she looked into his eyes, her own shimmering with tears.

'Goodbye, Michael.'

Taking Jamie by the hand, she helped him onto the train and they made their way along the carriage until they found two seats together. Whistles blew along the platform and the automatic doors closed with a hiss. There was no getting off now.

Michael was standing outside the window. He managed a smile and a wave for Jamie, and then his eyes locked with Rosalind's and his hand fell, forgotten, to his side. They were still staring desperately at each other as the train eased itself away from the station. Michael began walking alongside, to keep them in sight as long as possible, but he couldn't keep up. Frantically, Rosalind turned her head, turned round completely in her seat, but it was no good. The train just kept on picking up speed and bore her remorselessly away. It was over.

It felt very strange to be back in London. Rosalind had rung the chauffeur on her mobile the night before, and he met them at King's Cross. The voluptuously soft seats and darkened glass of the limousine only added to the air of unreality as they edged their stop-start way through the choked streets. Rosalind looked out of the window at the pale grey London buildings and the constant surge of traffic, the brisk, purposeful stride of crowds, and she ached to be back in the quiet, green lanes around Askerby.

Gripped by the same panicky sense of being in the wrong place, Rosalind wandered round the house later that evening. Compared to Maud's, it was palatial, impeccably designed and furnished. Everything worked, everything was clean and ordered, but it was just a house, not a home. Already, Rosalind was finding the luxury stifling. She had staff to clean, staff to cook, staff to open the door and fetch her a drink if she wanted one, staff to deal with her correspondence. She had nothing to do but try and distract a tired and fretful Jamie. 'I want Michael,' he had wept, clinging to her neck when she'd put him to bed, and Rosalind's heart had cracked.

'So do I, Jamie,' she had whispered. 'So do I.'

Now Rosalind sighed as she picked up the list of messages that her assistant had left for her. There was only one person she wanted to talk to, and he hadn't rung. For a moment she was tempted to ring Michael, just to hear his voice, but even as she picked up the phone she knew that it would be a mistake. They had said goodbye. She should just leave it at that. Slowly, carefully, Rosalind replaced the receiver. She would get used to missing him. She would have to.

But Rosalind didn't get used to it. Instead of getting easier to bear, the pain was worsening day by day, like a knife turning cruelly in her heart.

It wasn't as if she wasn't trying. Rosalind told herself that if she could just get back to being the person she had been before, she would begin to forget Michael.

Once she was expensively dressed and her hair had been properly styled, and highlighted to disguise the mousy brown beneath her natural copper colour, she would feel more like herself. Only she didn't. Rosalind looked at her sophisticated reflection and knew that no matter how she changed the way she looked, she couldn't change the way she was inside. She was still in love with Michael.

She tried not thinking about him, but that didn't work either. How could she not think about him when every fibre of her being ached to be with him again? When the nights were so long and so lonely without him, the days so empty? When Jamie talked constantly of Michael and Maud and asked where they were?

'You seem a bit down, Roz,' said Emma. Five days had dragged past, and Rosalind was sitting in Emma's kitchen, her hands cupped around a mug of coffee, her face drawn with tiredness. Emma looked at her in concern. 'You're not still upset about Simon, are you?'

Rosalind shook her head. 'Are you sure?' Emma was unconvinced. 'You must have been terribly hurt by the way he behaved.'

She had been, Rosalind remembered, but that had been the night Michael had made love to her. It was hard to believe now that Simon had mattered at all. 'I was at the time,' she told her friend, 'but I think I was humiliated rather than hurt. I know now that marrying Simon would have been a big mistake.'

Not the biggest. The biggest mistake she had made had been to turn Michael down all those years ago.

'I'm sorry if I'm a bit low,' she went on. 'I'm just…tired, I suppose.'

'Well, it sounds as if you had to work pretty hard up in Yorkshire,' said Emma, a little reassured. She divided the last of the coffee between the two mugs. 'Tell me about Michael,' she said casually. 'You've hardly mentioned him since you got back, and I never really heard how you got on. Was it very embarrassing pretending to be married to each other?'

Rosalind picked up her mug, then put it down again as she realised that her hands were shaking too much to hold it steady. 'No, it wasn't embarrassing.' Her throat was so tight that she could hardly speak, and Emma looked at her curiously.

'What was it like, then?'

'It was...' Rosalind thought about Michael, about the warmth of his hands and the smile in his eyes and the security of knowing that he was near. She thought about the long, enchanted nights and the feel of his arms around her. She thought about how he had brought her tea every morning, how they had sat up in bed with Jamie chattering between them and looked at each other over his small head.

'It was...' Her voice wavered and broke. Unable to go on, Rosalind pressed her hand to her mouth to try and stop her mouth trembling and turned her head away, but Emma had seen the tears that swam in the green eyes.

'Roz!' she exclaimed, horrified. 'What on earth is the matter?'

'It's Michael,' sobbed Rosalind, losing the battle to keep control and burying her face in her arms. 'I'm so in love with him, and I don't think I can bear it any more!'

It took Emma some time to coax the whole story out of Rosalind. When her distraught friend had eventually stumbled to an end, she blew out a long breath and patted Rosalind's back almost absently as she thought.

'How does Michael feel?' she asked at last. 'If you had such a wonderful time together, I can't believe it didn't mean anything to him.'

Rosalind mopped her face with a soggy tissue. 'He enjoyed it, but it didn't mean anything special. It was just chemistry.'

'I don't buy all that stuff about chemistry,' said Emma dryly. 'It sounds to me as if you were both just looking for an excuse not to admit that you'd fallen in love.'

'You don't understand,' she said, still tearful. 'We talked about it. We agreed that it was just going to be a temporary thing. Michael said that he didn't want to get emotionally involved again, and he doesn't. If he'd cared for me at all, he would have suggested that I stayed on for a while.' Rosalind sniffed and blew her nose. 'He couldn't wait to put me on the first train back to London!'

'Why should he ask you to stay if he didn't know you were in love with him?' Emma asked reasonably. 'Michael's got his pride, too. From what you've told me about what happened five years ago, I'd have thought he'd be very wary about being rejected all over again. I think it's up to you to go back and tell him how you feel.'

'I can't!'

'You can.' Emma put her hand over Rosalind's. 'It's taken you a long time to fall in love, Roz. Don't let it go without even trying to save it. All you have to do is tell Michael the truth. Last time he was the one who took the chance and told you he loved you. It's your turn this time. You owe him that, at least.'

Rosalind stood with her hand on the gate, looking at the house. Sick with nerves, she rehearsed what she would say, as she had been doing all the way in the taxi from York station. 'Just tell Michael the truth,' Emma had said, but what if he didn't want to hear it? What if he told her that it was too late? Why should he love her after all when not even her mother ever had?

Hopelessness swept over her, and Rosalind turned to call the taxi back. It had been stupid to come. It had been stupid to let herself fall in love in the first place. Hadn't she always known that it would end in hurt and tears?

But the taxi had gone, and she had nowhere else to go. Rosalind pushed open the gate and walked up to the door, ringing the bell before she had a chance to change her mind.

'Rosalind?' Maud's expression was oddly doubtful as she opened the door to find an elegantly dressed Rosalind standing on the step, her hair cut and coloured and her face carefully made up to bolster her courage.

'Yes, it's me.' Rosalind's carefully rehearsed explanation died on her lips, and she could only look back at Maud with anguish.

'You'll have come to see Michael,' said Maud, who had got over her surprise at Rosalind's transformation and was studying her thoughtfully. 'Are you going to tell him that you're in love with him?'

Rosalind nodded. 'Yes,' she said baldly, and Maud nodded as if satisfied.

'You'd better come in, then.' She stood back so that Rosalind could walk into the hall. 'What have you done with Jamie?' she asked as she closed the door.

'Emma's looking after him.' Rosalind hesitated. 'I wasn't sure what reception I would get. I wouldn't have blamed you if you'd refused to let me in the house after the way I deceived you, and made Michael deceive you, too. I'm really sorry,' she finished honestly. 'It wasn't fair to let you believe that you had an extra family when you didn't.'

'I was upset when Michael told me at first,' Maud admitted. 'I was hurt that you hadn't trusted me enough to tell me the truth. But once Michael had explained what you'd been through I understood why you had to keep it a secret. And it doesn't matter now that you're back, anyway. Are you staying this time?'

'That depends on Michael.' Rosalind drew a breath. 'Is he here?'

'He's out walking,' said Maud. 'He's done an awful lot of walking since you left,' she added dryly.

'Do you know which way he went?'

'Up to the woods, I think. He won't be long, though. Why don't you wait?'

Rosalind shook her head. 'I can't wait any longer,' she said.

Leaving her bag with Maud, she set off up the track she had walked so many times with Michael and Jamie. It was a warm spring afternoon and the air was spiced with the smell of wild garlic. The nervousness she had felt at the gate had given way to a strange sense of calm, and she walked steadily, certain that her feet would somehow take her to Michael. She didn't even hesitate at the fork, but followed the path that curved gently upwards.

And then, just past the old oak, there he was. He was walking down the path, head bent, shoulders hunched, his face set and tired. Rosalind did hesitate then, but only for a moment before she drew a long, steadying breath and moved forward to meet him. 'Hello, Michael,' she said quietly.

Michael's head jerked up at the sound of her voice

and he stopped dead, staring at her in disbelief. 'Rosalind?' he said, and the expression in his eyes dried the breath in her throat so that she could only nod speechlessly. 'What are you doing here?' He sounded dazed.

'I had to see you,' she managed to say.

'Is something wrong? Is it Jamie?'

'No, Jamie's fine.' Rosalind stopped. All her carefully prepared speeches had dissolved, along with the calm certainty that had carried her up the track, and now all she could do was stand and drink in the sight of him and wonder how she could begin to explain how much she loved him.

'I thought I'd never see you again,' Michael said suddenly. He walked forward until he was close enough to reach out and briefly touch Rosalind's hair, as if hardly daring to believe that she was real. 'I thought we'd said goodbye.'

'We did.' Rosalind's heart was hammering in her throat, making her voice unsteady. 'We said that there was nothing else to say, but it wasn't true,' she told him. '*I* still had something to say, but I didn't dare tell you while I was here.' She swallowed. 'I've spent the last five years regretting the things I said to you, Michael. I don't want to spend the next five regretting something I didn't say.'

'What was it?' said Michael, almost as if he was bracing himself against the answer.

Rosalind looked at him. 'I came back to tell you that I love you,' she said simply.

It was very quiet in the woods. Somewhere, she could hear a bird calling high in the trees, but otherwise there was nothing but the desperate beat of her heart.

'You love me?' said Michael slowly, disbelievingly.

'Yes.'

'But…you don't believe in love,' he reminded her.

'I didn't,' she admitted. 'I didn't want to believe in it. Ever since my mother left I've been afraid of loving someone and being hurt again, but since I've met you again I've learnt that loving isn't something you can choose not to do.' She took a steadying breath. 'I don't know if I was in love with you or not five years ago, Michael, but I'm in love with you now. I tried to deny it, I tried to hide it and I tried to forget it, but I couldn't.'

She paused. Michael was holding himself almost warily, but he was listening. 'We talked about the chemistry between us, and when you said that what we had was just a physical thing I agreed, because I thought that was all you wanted, but it wasn't, Michael. Not for me, not this time.'

'What *was* it for you?' Michael asked at last, and Rosalind thought for a while before answering. She knew what it was, but whether she could find the words to describe it was another matter, and somehow she had to convince him that what she felt was real.

'It was wanting to be with you, not just in bed but all the time, and feeling happy and safe and somehow more *alive* when I was. It was a room being empty when you weren't in it. It was looking at you and knowing that without you a piece of me would always be missing…' Rosalind trailed off. 'It still is all those things, Michael,' she went on after a moment. 'I know there's no reason why you should believe me after the way I treated you, but it's true. I'm in love with you.'

She tried to smile, but it didn't really work properly. 'I just had to tell you,' she said. 'Now's your chance to throw everything back in my face, just like I did to you five years ago. There would be a sort of poetic justice to it, wouldn't there?'

Michael found his voice at last. 'You don't really think I'd do that, do you?' he asked in a deep voice that set her trembling.

'I wouldn't blame you if you did.'

'Rosalind.' Michael savoured the sound of her name in his mouth as he reached out and took her hands in a firm, warm clasp. 'Rosalind, don't you know what it means to hear you say that you love me? Don't you know how much I love you, how much I've always loved you?'

Her fingers clung to his, her heart thudding with hope at the expression in his grey eyes. 'But I was so horrible to you!'

'It doesn't make any difference how you are,' he told her. 'I've seen you cold and cross and cruel, and I've seen you warm and loving and kind, and I love you just the same.' His hands gripped hers tightly. 'I didn't want to love you either, Rosalind, but I couldn't do a damn thing about it. I fell hopelessly in love with you five years ago and I've loved you ever since.'

'You said you were just obsessed with me before,' Rosalind reminded him, still hardly daring to let herself believe that everything was going to be all right. 'You said it was just a physical attraction.'

'I said a lot of things I didn't mean,' said Michael ruefully. 'I only said that because I didn't want you to know that I'd spent the last five years dreaming about you. I'd tell myself that I'd forgotten you, and that I was much better off with a girl like Kathy, but it never worked.'

'I was so jealous when Emma told me about Kathy,'

she confessed. 'She sounded so nice and suitable for you.'

Michael smiled, releasing her fingers so that he could let his hands drift lovingly up her arms and over her shoulders to her throat. 'She was,' he said. 'She was everything I should ever have wanted in a woman. But she wasn't a girl whose slightest touch could set me on fire. She wasn't a girl whose smile shimmered in my mind long after she had gone.' He trapped her face between her palms and looked deep into her eyes. 'She wasn't you,' he said softly, and kissed her.

As his lips touched hers, Rosalind dissolved in a cascade of intense joy. It poured through her, rinsing away all the misery and doubt, leaving in its wake a glow of golden enchantment. She clung to him, kissing him back almost frantically, while Michael let go of her face and wrapped his arms around her so that he could gather her closer and kiss her as if he would never let her go.

'It was only ever you, Rosalind,' Michael told her, resting his cheek against her shining hair at last. 'It will only ever be you.'

The relief of knowing that he loved her was so exquisite that it was almost painful. Rosalind burrowed into him, her arms tight around his waist, her face pressed into his throat. 'Oh, Michael, if only I'd married you five years ago! We've wasted so much time.'

Michael kissed her hair. 'I think perhaps we needed to spend that time apart, to realise just what we've got and how special it is,' he said. 'We were too young to know that we'd found the only person we'd ever be happy with. I spent years telling myself that I hated you for making me love you when you didn't care, but all you had to do was walk into Emma's sitting room that day and I started to fall in love with you all over again.'

He drew back a little, lifting Rosalind's face so that he could smile into her shining green eyes. 'Only this time I loved you so much more,' he said, in a voice that made her shiver with happiness. 'I'd fallen in love with your beauty before, and when I left it was your beauty I missed. I missed your perfume and the feel of your skin and the way your lashes tilted when you smiled.

'I still love all those things about you,' Michael went on, caressing her cheek with his warm thumb, 'but I love the Rosalind you kept hidden before as well. I didn't know how warm and brave and vulnerable you were until I met you again. I've missed you so badly since I put you on that damned train last week. I thought I'd been missing you for the last five years, but this time it was much worse. This time I missed the way you cuddle Jamie. I missed the impatient way you push your hair behind your ears, and that gritty look you get when you don't want to do something but you're not going to let yourself be beaten by it! I missed everything about you, Rosalind,' he confessed. 'I don't ever want to miss you again.'

Rosalind's eyes were starry with tears. 'Then don't let me go,' she whispered, and his mouth came down on hers.

'I won't,' Michael promised, and kissed her again.

Much later, Rosalind heaved a sigh of contentment and leant into him, nuzzling his throat. 'Why didn't you tell me you loved me before I went back to London?'

'I didn't know that *you* loved *me,*' Michael pointed out, holding her close. 'There were times when I let myself hope that you might feel more than you had done before, but you seemed happy to accept that we would just have a couple of weeks together. Then I'd remember how upset you were about Simon, and I'd wonder if making love with me had just been a way of getting your own back on him.'

Rosalind lifted her head. 'It was *never* that, Michael, you must know that,' she said urgently, and he pulled her back against him.

'I do now,' he said, 'but at the time I was afraid that you cared more for Simon than you were admitting, and that all you really wanted from me was comfort. And I suppose I thought too about the last time I told you I loved you,' he went on slowly. 'Whenever I was about to pluck up the courage to tell you that I was still in love with you, I'd remember what you'd said then, about how different our lives were, and I'd realise that they still were.' His voice changed slightly. 'They still are different, Rosalind.'

'Mine's changed,' she said, tipping her head back to look at him. 'I went back to my old life last week and I realised that none of it meant anything without you. My life is with you and with Jamie now. I don't care where we are or what we do as long as we're together.'

'In that case, I think I'd better ask you to marry me again, don't you?' said Michael with an unsteady smile. Cupping her face between his hands, he kissed the corner of her mouth. 'Tell me you love me again first,' he murmured as he kissed first the other corner and then the tip of her nose and her eyes before teasing a devastating line of kisses from temple to ear and on along her jaw back to her lips. 'I want to hear you say it again.'

'I love you, Michael,' said Rosalind shakily. 'I do, I do, I do!'

'And you'll marry me?'

'Yes,' she breathed against his mouth. 'Oh, yes, I will!'

Then there were no more words for a very long time

as they kissed and kissed again until they were breathless and giddy with delight. Awash with happiness, Rosalind melted into the intoxicating hardness of Michael's body. 'Are you sure I'm not dreaming?' she murmured blissfully between kisses. 'I've been so miserable, and now I'm so happy…I can't believe you really love me!'

'I do,' said Michael, smiling as he kissed her again. 'I do, I do, I do!'

It was much, much later before they walked hand in hand back down the path. 'Maud must be wondering what on earth's happened to us,' exclaimed Rosalind when she realised what time it was.

'I should think she's got a pretty good idea,' said Michael. 'Maud's no fool. She knows how much I've been missing you—and Jamie. I think she missed you, too. The house was so empty without you. *Life* was empty without you.'

They stopped at the end of the track to look at the village basking peacefully in the slanting evening sunshine. 'God, it's hard to remember how desperate I was when I came out this afternoon,' he went on, putting his arm around Rosalind and holding her tight against him, to reassure himself that she was really there. 'I'd been walking round and round in circles for hours, trying to decide what to do. I've only got a couple of days before I'm due to fly back, and I didn't know if I could bear not to be in the same country as you at least. I thought about applying for a post back in the UK—there are several good ones going up in the North—but then I wondered whether that wouldn't be worse. I might be near you, but I still wouldn't be able to see you or hold you.'

'Oh, Michael, it would have been terrible!' Rosalind

shuddered at how close they had come to missing each other again.

'Yes, it would,' he agreed, kissing her. 'But it won't be now.'

'Do you really have to go back in two days?' she asked as she put her arms round his neck and kissed him back.

'I'll change my flight,' said Michael. 'It won't make that much difference to the site if I stay a little while longer—long enough to get married, anyway. I'm not leaving you behind again.' Then he hesitated. 'Am I taking too much for granted, Rosalind? You might not want to get married in a rush like that. Come to that, you might not want to bring Jamie out to the desert. Perhaps we should wait until I come home—'

'No,' Rosalind interrupted him firmly. 'All Jamie and I want is to be with you. I don't want a big wedding, Michael. Why don't we ask Emma to bring Jamie up tomorrow? We can get married up here as soon as we can and Maud can come to our wedding after all. If the people who care about us most are there, what else do we need?'

'Just a ring,' said Michael, smiling, 'and we've already got that.' He dug in his pocket. 'Look,' he said, bringing out the wedding ring she had given him back the day she'd left for London. 'I've been carrying this round with me just so that I could hold it in my hand and know that you'd worn it.' He grimaced at the memory of his own desperation. 'I even told myself I could still feel the warmth of your skin.'

Rosalind took the ring and held it on her palm, just as she had done in the motorway service station. Had it only been a month ago? '"With this ring I thee disguise",' she murmured, remembering the brusque way

Michael had pushed it onto her finger, and she smiled into his eyes. 'It'll be different this time, won't it, Michael?'

'It will,' Michael promised. 'This time it will be for real.'

'Yes,' sighed Rosalind happily as he kissed her again. 'This time it will be for ever.'